Connected 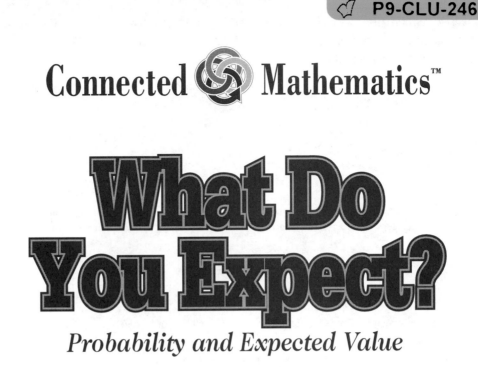 Mathematics™

What Do You Expect?

Probability and Expected Value

Teacher's Guide

Glenda Lappan
James T. Fey
William M. Fitzgerald
Susan N. Friel
Elizabeth Difanis Phillips

Prentice Hall

Glenview, Illinois
Needham, Massachusetts
Upper Saddle River, New Jersey

Connected Mathematics™ was developed at Michigan State University with financial support from the Michigan State University Office of the Provost, Computing and Technology, and the College of Natural Science.

This material is based upon work supported by the National Science Foundation under Grant No. MDR 9150217.

This project was supported, in part,
by the
National Science Foundation
Opinions expressed are those of the authors
and not necessarily those of the Foundation

The Michigan State University authors and administration have agreed that all MSU royalties arising from this publication will be devoted to purposes supported by the Department of Mathematics and the MSU Mathematics Education Enrichment Fund.

Photo Acknowledgements: 27 © William Carter/Photo Researchers, Inc.; 29 © Mitch Wojnarowicz/The Image Works; 33 © Topham/The Image Works; 34 © Peter Menzel/Stock, Boston; 47 © James Carroll/Stock, Boston; 50 © Carl Sissac/*Sports Illustrated*; 54 © Shelley Gazin/The Image Works; 56 © Mitch Wojnarowicz/The Image Works; 57 © Bob Daemmrich/Stock, Boston; 61 © Tim Davis/Photo Researchers, Inc.; 69 © Renee Lynn/Photo Researchers, Inc.; 74 © Rapho/Photo Researchers, Inc.

Quotation: Page 50, reprinted courtesy of Sports Illustrated:
"Sports People: Don Calhoun" by Lisa Bessone, SI,
April 26, 1993, Copyright © 1993, Time Inc. All rights reserved.

ISBN 0-13-053106-5
2 3 4 5 6 7 8 9 10   05 04 03 02 01

The Connected Mathematics Project Staff

Project Directors

James T. Fey
University of Maryland

William M. Fitzgerald
Michigan State University

Susan N. Friel
University of North Carolina at Chapel Hill

Glenda Lappan
Michigan State University

Elizabeth Difanis Phillips
Michigan State University

Project Manager

Kathy Burgis
Michigan State University

Technical Coordinator

Judith Martus Miller
Michigan State University

Collaborating Teachers/Writers

Mary K. Bouck
Portland, Michigan

Jacqueline Stewart
Okemos, Michigan

Curriculum Development Consultants

David Ben-Chaim
Weizmann Institute

Alex Friedlander
Weizmann Institute

Eleanor Geiger
University of Maryland

Jane Mitchell
University of North Carolina at Chapel Hill

Anthony D. Rickard
Alma College

Evaluation Team

Mark Hoover
Michigan State University

Diane V. Lambdin
Indiana University

Sandra K. Wilcox
Michigan State University

Judith S. Zawojewski
National-Louis University

Graduate Assistants

Scott J. Baldridge
Michigan State University

Angie S. Eshelman
Michigan State University

M. Faaiz Gierdien
Michigan State University

Jane M. Keiser
Indiana University

Angela S. Krebs
Michigan State University

James M. Larson
Michigan State University

Ronald Preston
Indiana University

Tat Ming Sze
Michigan State University

Sarah Theule-Lubienski
Michigan State University

Jeffrey J. Wanko
Michigan State University

Field Test Production Team

Katherine Oesterle
Michigan State University

Stacey L. Otto
University of North Carolina at Chapel Hill

Teacher/Assessment Team

Kathy Booth
Waverly, Michigan

Anita Clark
Marshall, Michigan

Julie Faulkner
Traverse City, Michigan

Theodore Gardella
Bloomfield Hills, Michigan

Yvonne Grant
Portland, Michigan

Linda R. Lobue
Vista, California

Suzanne McGrath
Chula Vista, California

Nancy McIntyre
Troy, Michigan

Mary Beth Schmitt
Traverse City, Michigan

Linda Walker
Tallahassee, Florida

Software Developer

Richard Burgis
East Lansing, Michigan

Development Center Directors

Nicholas Branca
San Diego State University

Dianne Briars
Pittsburgh Public Schools

Frances R. Curcio
New York University

Perry Lanier
Michigan State University

J. Michael Shaughnessy
Portland State University

Charles Vonder Embse
Central Michigan University

Field Test Coordinators

Michelle Bohan
Queens, New York

Melanie Branca
San Diego, California

Alecia Devantier
Shepherd, Michigan

Jenny Jorgensen
Flint, Michigan

Sandra Kralovec
Portland, Oregon

Sonia Marsalis
Flint, Michigan

William Schaeffer
Pittsburgh, Pennsylvania

Karma Vince
Toledo, Ohio

Virginia Wolf
Pittsburgh, Pennsylvania

Shirel Yaloz
Queens, New York

Student Assistants

Laura Hammond
David Roche
Courtney Stoner
Jovan Trpovski
Julie Valicenti
Michigan State University

Patricia Wagner
Holmes Middle School

Greg Williams
Gundry Elementary School

Lansing

Susan Bissonette
Waverly Middle School

Kathy Booth
Waverly East Intermediate School

Carole Campbell
Waverly East Intermediate School

Gary Gillespie
Waverly East Intermediate School

Denise Kehren
Waverly Middle School

Virginia Larson
Waverly East Intermediate School

Kelly Martin
Waverly Middle School

Laurie Metevier
Waverly East Intermediate School

Craig Paksi
Waverly East Intermediate School

Tony Pecoraro
Waverly Middle School

Helene Rewa
Waverly East Intermediate School

Arnold Stiefel
Waverly Middle School

Portland

Bill Carlton
Portland Middle School

Kathy Dole
Portland Middle School

Debby Flate
Portland Middle School

Yvonne Grant
Portland Middle School

Terry Keusch
Portland Middle School

John Manzini
Portland Middle School

Mary Parker
Portland Middle School

Scott Sandborn
Portland Middle School

Shepherd

Steve Brant
Shepherd Middle School

Marty Brock
Shepherd Middle School

Cathy Church
Shepherd Middle School

Ginny Crandall
Shepherd Middle School

Craig Ericksen
Shepherd Middle School

Natalie Hackney
Shepherd Middle School

Bill Hamilton
Shepherd Middle School

Julie Salisbury
Shepherd Middle School

Sturgis

Sandra Allen
Eastwood Elementary School

Margaret Baker
Eastwood Elementary School

Steven Baker
Eastwood Elementary School

Keith Barnes
Sturgis Middle School

Wilodean Beckwith
Eastwood Elementary School

Darcy Bird
Eastwood Elementary School

Bill Dickey
Sturgis Middle School

Ellen Eisele
Sturgis Middle School

James Hoelscher
Sturgis Middle School

Richard Nolan
Sturgis Middle School

J. Hunter Raiford
Sturgis Middle School

Cindy Sprowl
Eastwood Elementary School

Leslie Stewart
Eastwood Elementary School

Connie Sutton
Eastwood Elementary School

Traverse City

Maureen Bauer
Interlochen Elementary School

Ivanka Berskshire
East Junior High School

Sarah Boehm
Courtade Elementary School

Marilyn Conklin
Interlochen Elementary School

Nancy Crandall
Blair Elementary School

Fran Cullen
Courtade Elementary School

Eric Dreier
Old Mission Elementary School

Lisa Dzierwa
Cherry Knoll Elementary School

Ray Fouch
West Junior High School

Ed Hargis
Willow Hill Elementary School

Richard Henry
West Junior High School

Dessie Hughes
Cherry Knoll Elementary School

Ruthanne Kladder
Oak Park Elementary School

Bonnie Knapp
West Junior High School

Sue Laisure
Sabin Elementary School

Stan Malaski
Oak Park Elementary School

Jody Meyers
Sabin Elementary School

Marsha Myles
East Junior High School

Mary Beth O'Neil
Traverse Heights Elementary School

Jan Palkowski
East Junior High School

Karen Richardson
Old Mission Elementary School

Kristin Sak
Bertha Vos Elementary School

Mary Beth Schmitt
East Junior High School

Mike Schrotenboer
Norris Elementary School

Gail Smith
Willow Hill Elementary School

Karrie Tufts
Eastern Elementary School

Mike Wilson
East Junior High School

Tom Wilson
West Junior High School

Minnesota

Minneapolis

Betsy Ford
Northeast Middle School

New York

East Elmhurst

Allison Clark
Louis Armstrong Middle School

Dorothy Hershey
Louis Armstrong Middle School

J. Lewis McNeece
Louis Armstrong Middle School

Rossana Perez
Louis Armstrong Middle School

Merna Porter
Louis Armstrong Middle School

Marie Turini
Louis Armstrong Middle School

North Carolina

Durham

Everly Broadway
Durham Public Schools

Thomas Carson
Duke School for Children

Mary Hebrank
Duke School for Children

Bill O'Connor
Duke School for Children

Ruth Pershing
Duke School for Children

Peter Reichert
Duke School for Children

Elizabeth City

Rita Banks
Elizabeth City Middle School

Beth Chaundry
Elizabeth City Middle School

Amy Cuthbertson
Elizabeth City Middle School

Deni Dennison
Elizabeth City Middle School

Jean Gray
Elizabeth City Middle School

John McMenamin
Elizabeth City Middle School

Nicollette Nixon
Elizabeth City Middle School

Malinda Norfleet
Elizabeth City Middle School

Joyce O'Neal
Elizabeth City Middle School

Clevie Sawyer
Elizabeth City Middle School

Juanita Shannon
Elizabeth City Middle School

Terry Thorne
Elizabeth City Middle School

Rebecca Wardour
Elizabeth City Middle School

Leora Winslow
Elizabeth City Middle School

Franklinton

Susan Haywood
Franklinton Elementary School

Clyde Melton
Franklinton Elementary School

Louisburg

Lisa Anderson
Terrell Lane Middle School

Jackie Frazier
Terrell Lane Middle School

Pam Harris
Terrell Lane Middle School

Ohio

Toledo

Bonnie Bias
Hawkins Elementary School

Marsha Jackish
Hawkins Elementary School

Lee Jagodzinski
DeVeaux Junior High School

Norma J. King
Old Orchard Elementary School

Margaret McCready
Old Orchard Elementary School

Carmella Morton
DeVeaux Junior High School

Karen C. Rohrs
Hawkins Elementary School

Marie Sahloff
DeVeaux Junior High School

L. Michael Vince
McTigue Junior High School

Brenda D. Watkins
Old Orchard Elementary School

Oregon

Canby

Sandra Kralovec
Ackerman Middle School

Portland

Roberta Cohen
Catlin Gabel School

David Ellenberg
Catlin Gabel School

Sara Normington
Catlin Gabel School

Karen Scholte-Arce
Catlin Gabel School

West Linn

Marge Burack
Wood Middle School

Tracy Wygant
Athey Creek Middle School

Pennsylvania

Pittsburgh

Sheryl Adams
Reizenstein Middle School

Sue Barie
Frick International Studies Academy

Suzie Berry
Frick International Studies Academy

Richard Delgrosso
Frick International Studies Academy

Janet Falkowski
Frick International Studies Academy

Joanne George
Reizenstein Middle School

Harriet Hopper
Reizenstein Middle School

Chuck Jessen
Reizenstein Middle School

Ken Labuskes
Reizenstein Middle School

Barbara Lewis
Reizenstein Middle School

Sharon Mihalich
Reizenstein Middle School

Marianne O'Connor
Frick International Studies Academy

Mark Sammartino
Reizenstein Middle School

Washington

Seattle

Chris Johnson
University Preparatory Academy

Rick Purn
University Preparatory Academy

Contents

What Do You Expect? is the second probability unit in the Connected Mathematics™ curriculum. Through their work in this unit, students will deepen their understanding of the basic concepts of probability. They will develop several powerful strategies for finding and interpreting experimental and theoretical probabilities, such as using simulations to gather experimental data; using counting trees and other listing techniques to determine all the possible outcomes in a situation; and creating area models, in which the probability of each possible outcome is represented as portion of the whole. In addition, students will use area models to determine probabilities in two-stage situations and to informally develop an understanding of expected value, or long-term average.

The work in this unit assumes that students are familiar with the basic ideas of probability that are presented in the grade 6 unit *How Likely Is It?* If some or all of your students have not explored the concepts covered in that unit, you will need to prepare them for the mathematics they will encounter in *What Do You Expect?* Spend a few days on Investigations 1 through 4 of *How Likely Is It?*, or an alternative presentation, to expose students to the basics of probability. The mathematics with which students should be familiar are described in the next section.

If your students have studied *How Likely Is It?*, Investigations 1 and 2 of this unit should serve as a sufficient review, as well as an extension, of the ideas with which they are already acquainted.

The Mathematics in *What Do You Expect?*

Following is a summary of the basic ideas that are covered in the grade 6 probability unit, *How Likely Is It?*, and descriptions of the new mathematical ideas students will encounter in *What Do You Expect?*

Basic Probability Concepts

The term *probability* is applied to situations that have uncertain outcomes on individual trials but a predictable pattern of outcomes over many trials. For example, when we toss a fair coin, we are uncertain whether it will come up heads or tails; but we do know that, over the long run, we will get heads about half of the time and tails about half of the time. This does not mean that we can't get several heads in a row, or that if we get heads on one toss we are more likely to get tails on the next. This concept—uncertainty on an individual outcome but predictable regularity in the long run—is often difficult for students. Students often need a variety of experiences that challenge their prior conceptions before they grasp this basic concept of probability.

If we toss a tack into the air, we know that it will land either on its head or its side. If we toss a tack many times, we can use the ratio of the number of times it lands on its side to the total number of tosses to estimate the likelihood that the tack will land on its side. Since this ratio is found by experimentation, it is called an *experimental probability*. Many uses of probability in daily life, such as weather forecasts and sports predictions, are based on experimental probabilities.

This unit offers many opportunities for students to collect data through experimentation and to use their data to assign experimental probabilities to the possible outcomes. It is important for students to realize that a small amount of data may contain a wide variation among the samples, and that only through experimentation over many trials can good estimates be made about what will happen in the long run. In other words, experimental probabilities must be based on a great number of trials relative to the number of possible outcomes.

In some situations, such as tossing a fair coin, we can also find *theoretical probabilities*. We know that a fair coin will land either heads up or tails up and that each outcome is *equally likely*. As there are two equally likely outcomes, the probability that a fair coin will land heads up is 1 out of 2, or $\frac{1}{2}$. In general, the theoretical probability that a coin will land heads up can be expressed as follows:

$$P(\text{head}) = \frac{\text{number of favorable outcomes}}{\text{number of possible outcomes}} = \frac{1 \text{ (there is 1 head on a coin)}}{2 \text{ (there are 2 equally likely outcomes)}}$$

Another example of a situation for which we can find a theoretical probability is the rolling of a six-sided number cube. The six possible outcomes—1, 2, 3, 4, 5, and 6—are each equally likely to occur on any single roll. Thus, $P(1) = P(2) = P(3) = P(4) = P(5) = P(6) = \frac{1}{6}$. We can use this theoretical probability to estimate that if a number cube is rolled many times, we could expect each number to be rolled about $\frac{1}{6}$ of the time.

Probabilities, whether obtained through theoretical analysis or experimentation, are useful for *predicting* what should happen over the long run. Yet, a probability does not tell us exactly what will happen. For example, if we toss a coin 40 times, we may not get exactly 20 heads; but if we toss a coin 1000 times, the ratio of heads will be fairly close to $\frac{1}{2}$. Experimental data gathered over many trials should produce probabilities that are close to the theoretical probabilities; this idea is sometimes called the Law of Large Numbers. If we can calculate a theoretical probability, we can use it to predict what will happen in the long run rather than having to rely on experimentation alone.

Theoretical Probability Models

Students who have studied the grade 6 probability unit *How Likely Is It?* have already learned quite a bit about conducting simulations to find experimental probabilities and making organized lists of possible outcomes to find theoretical probabilities. In this unit, they will continue to work with these familiar strategies, while learning two new strategies for finding theoretical probabilities: making counting trees to list all possible outcomes, and constructing area models to represent the possible outcomes.

Counting Trees

Counting trees, introduced in Investigation 1 and used throughout the unit, offer students a way to determine all the possible outcomes in a situation systematically. For example, suppose a spinner divided into three equal sections is spun and a six-sided number cube is rolled.

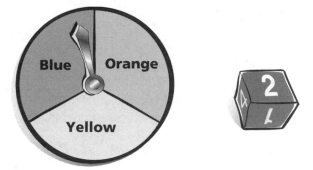

The possible outcomes can be shown in a list and a counting tree.

Spinner	Number cube
blue	1
blue	2
blue	3
blue	4
blue	5
blue	6
orange	1
orange	2
orange	3
orange	4
orange	5
orange	6
yellow	1
yellow	2
yellow	3
yellow	4
yellow	5
yellow	6

Spinner

Number cube

Outcome

start

blue
1 — blue/1
2 — blue/2
3 — blue/3
4 — blue/4
5 — blue/5
6 — blue/6

orange
1 — orange/1
2 — orange/2
3 — orange/3
4 — orange/4
5 — orange/5
6 — orange/6

yellow
1 — yellow/1
2 — yellow/2
3 — yellow/3
4 — yellow/4
5 — yellow/5
6 — yellow/6

In this unit, students use counting trees to find the number of equally likely outcomes in situations with a great number of possible outcomes. Counting trees are particularly useful for listing outcomes in situations involving a series of actions, such as rolling a number cube twice or rolling two number cubes; tossing a coin four times or tossing four coins; or choosing several items from a menu, such as a sandwich, a drink, and a dessert.

Counting trees can be used as a basis for understanding the multiplication of probabilities, though they are not intended to be used that way in this unit. Students do not yet understand enough about probability to know when and why it is appropriate to multiply probabilities. (Some of the ACE extension questions, however, are much easier to answer if students have discovered the idea of multiplying probabilities.)

Area Models

In *How Likely Is It?*, students divided the area of circular spinners to represent probabilities. Investigation 3 of *What Do You Expect?* lays the groundwork for thinking about probabilities in terms of area on a grid.

Area models, like counting trees, are useful for finding probabilities in situations involving successive actions, such as a basketball player who is allowed to attempt a second free throw only if the first succeeds. Unlike counting trees, an area model is particularly powerful in situations in which the possible outcomes are *not* equally likely. Whereas students will use counting trees to help determine the possible equally likely outcomes in a situation, area models will help them find and represent probabilities of outcomes that are not equally likely, as in multistage situations.

The area model below is a square divided to show the probability that a 60% free-throw shooter will score 0, 1, or 2 points in a two-shot free-throw situation in basketball. In a two-shot situation, the player will get to attempt a second free throw whether or not the first free throw succeeds.

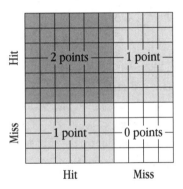

Expected Value

The long-term aspect of probability is a powerful concept. Rather than *guarantee* what will happen on a particular trial or even in the short run, probability models *predict* what will happen in the long run over many trials. Often, this is the most valuable information we can gain about a probability situation: a prediction of the expected value of the situation. The *expected value* is a long-term average of the probability of each outcome weighted by the payoff for that outcome.

In this unit, students are introduced to expected value in an informal yet concrete way. We do not expect them to develop a formal definition of expected value or to use a formula for finding it. In fact, students might never use the term *expected value* in their work in this unit, instead thinking of the concept as "what to expect in the long run." Expected value goes one step beyond basic probabilities because it incorporates the value—such as points earned in a game or money won in a contest—attached to each possible outcome in computing how many points or dollars we can expect to average per game or contest in the long run.

For example, consider the simple situation of a breeder of Labrador retrievers. Each male puppy will be sold for $200, and each female puppy will be sold for $250. In the long run, how much could the breeder expect to average per puppy?

We can approach the problem by analyzing a specific number of cases; let's say 50 puppies born. Assuming that the probability of a male puppy is $\frac{1}{2}$ and of a female puppy is $\frac{1}{2}$, the breeder could expect about 25 puppies of each sex. This means the breeder could expect to collect $25 \times \$200 = \$5000$ for the male puppies and $25 \times \$250 = \$6250$ for the female puppies, for a total of $11,250. The average amount per puppy is thus $\$11,250 \div 50 = \$225$.

We could also arrive at this result by the computation $\frac{1}{2}(\$250) + \frac{1}{2}(\$200) = \$225$, which shows each payoff weighted (multiplied) by the probability that it will occur. This strategy is closer to the mathematical definition of expected value but more conceptually difficult for students. (This idea is not directly addressed in this unit.)

Independent and Dependent Events

Toward the end of this unit, the idea of independent and dependent events is introduced informally. This concept, a difficult one, is often a major focus of probability study in high school and college courses. Yet, we feel it is important to introduce this concept because many students working through a basic probability unit such as this one develop the belief that *all* events are independent.

Suppose you twice draw a marble from a bag containing two red marbles and two blue marbles. If you *replace* the selected marble after the first draw, the two draws will be *independent* of each other, because what you draw the first time will not affect what you draw the second time. If you *do not replace* the selected marble, the second draw will be *dependent* on the first draw, because the probability of drawing each color the second time depends on the color chosen on the first draw. For example, if you draw a red marble the first time and do not replace it, the probability of drawing a red marble the second time is $\frac{1}{3}$ rather than $\frac{1}{2}$.

In this unit, students analyze dependent events by using the situation to help make sense of the sequence of actions. They look at the context and determine the sequence of actions and the possibilities at each step in the sequence. The steps in the sequence guide the apportioning of the total area in an area model, or the designing of a counting tree representing all possible outcomes. Then, each portion of area in an area model, or each path on a counting tree, is compared to the total area or the total number of possible outcomes to form probability statements.

As students use an area model to make sense of two-stage probability situations, take any opportunity to help those who show readiness to see the connection to multiplying probabilities. As an area model is also used to develop an understanding of the multiplication of fractions, many students will see this connection naturally.

Mathematical and Problem-Solving Goals

What Do You Expect? was created to help students

- Review and come to a deeper understanding of experimental and theoretical probabilities and the relationship between them

- Review and further develop an understanding of the possible outcomes in a situation

- Review and come to a deeper understanding of the distinction between equally likely and non–equally likely outcomes

- Understand the distinction between single, specific outcomes and sets of outcomes that comprise an event

- Analyze situations involving independent events

- Analyze situations involving dependent events

- Understand how to use probabilities and equivalent fractions to find expected value

- Determine whether games of chance are fair or unfair and find ways to make unfair games fair

- Develop a variety of strategies for analyzing probabilities, such as using lists, counting trees, and area models

- Use counting trees for finding theoretical probabilities in binomial, or 50-50, probability situations

- Determine the expected value of a chance situation

- Use probability and expected value to make decisions

- Find probabilities in situations that involve drawing with and without replacement

The overall goal of the Connected Mathematics curriculum is to help students develop sound mathematical habits. Through their work in this and other probability units, students learn important questions to ask themselves about any situation that can be represented and modeled mathematically, such as: *In what types of situations can probability be used to help make a decision? What are the possible outcomes for this situation? What techniques can be used to list all the possible outcomes? Are the outcomes equally likely? Can theoretical probabilities be calculated, or do I need to find experimental probabilities? How can I tell whether these events are independent or dependent? Is this game fair? If it is not fair, how can the rules or the scoring system be changed to make it fair? If this game is played several times, what will be the expected value, or the average payoff?*

Investigation 1: Evaluating Games of Chance

Students explore games that involve drawing colored blocks from a bucket and spinning spinners. In the process of analyzing the games, they review some of the basic concepts of probability that are developed in the grade 6 probability unit, *How Likely Is It?*—equally likely events, experimental and theoretical probabilities, and using probabilities to estimate the chance that a specific outcome will occur. Students use counting trees and other types of lists to determine all the possible outcomes in a given game. The ACE questions offer many opportunities for reviewing these concepts.

Investigation 2: Analyzing Number-Cube Games

Students explore games that involve rolling two number cubes and computing the sum or product of the numbers that are rolled. In the process, they continue to review some of the basic concepts of probability, including finding experimental probabilities, listing outcomes to find theoretical probabilities, comparing experimental probabilities with theoretical probabilities, and deciding whether a game is fair.

Investigation 3: Probability and Area

In the context of a computer game, students are introduced to relating probabilities to the area of a grid, which helps prepare them for analyzing probabilities using the area model introduced in Investigation 4. Additionally, students continue to think about other probability concepts, such as equally likely versus non–equally likely outcomes. Connections to geometry are embedded throughout the investigation and the ACE questions.

Investigation 4: Analyzing Two-Stage Games

Students encounter probability situations in which one event depends on another. They use an area model to analyze the probabilities of two or more such *dependent events*. In these problems, the outcomes are not equally likely, so a simple listing of the possible outcomes will not work.

Investigation 5: Expected Value

Students use spinners to simulate free-throw situations in basketball and employ area models to find the probabilities involved with players who have different free-throw averages. Students are formally introduced to the concept of *expected value*, or long-term average.

Investigation 6: Carnival Games

As students analyze a variety of proposed carnival games, they apply and extend strategies and ideas from earlier investigations. They continue to develop techniques for conducting simulations, analyzing situations to find all possible outcomes, and finding expected value to determine the profitability of a game. Students also confront the issue of how the dependence of the outcomes of one action on another action affects the probabilities in a situation.

Investigation 7: Analyzing Sequences of Outcomes

Students investigate two problems that are essentially the same mathematically. Predicting the sex of puppies in a litter and guessing on a true-false quiz are both binomial events. In each problem, students use counting trees to analyze sequences of equally likely outcomes. In the process, they confront several common misconceptions about binomial events. For example, the birth of a male, a female, a male, and a female puppy, in that order, is just as likely as the birth of four females; but two males and two females in any order is more likely than four females.

Materials

For students

■ Labsheets

■ Graphing calculators

■ Number cubes (2 per pair)

■ 10-sided number cubes (optional)

■ Colored blocks or other manipulatives (4 of one color and 2 of another color for each pair of students)

■ Opaque containers large enough for a student's hand (2 identical containers per group)

■ Computers and the Treasure Hunt program (optional; see Technology on the next page)

■ Angle rulers (optional)

■ 10-section, 12-section, and 16-section spinners (optional; provided as blackline masters)

■ 10 by 10 grids (optional; provided as blackline masters)

■ Grid paper (optional; provided as a blackline master)

■ Large sheets of paper (optional; for displaying answers)

■ Paper clips or bobby pins (for spinners; 1 per pair)

■ Coins (1 per group)

For the teacher

■ Transparencies and transparency markers (optional)

■ Transparencies of Labsheets 1.2, 1.3, and 5.2 (optional)

■ Transparent 10 by 10 grid (optional; copy the blackline master onto transparency film)

■ Opaque container filled with 4 blue, 8 yellow, and 12 red blocks (substitute other colors or objects if necessary)

■ 16 additional blue blocks

The ideas in *What Do You Expect?* build on and connect to several big ideas in other Connected Mathematics units.

Big Idea	Prior Work	Future Work
understanding probability	understanding chance as the likelihood of a particular event occurring; studying equally likely outcomes and randomness (*How Likely Is It?*); interpreting decimals, fractions, and percents as probabilities (*Bits and Pieces II*)	using probabilities to make inferences and predictions about populations based on analysis of population samples (*Samples and Populations*)
understanding, determining, and reasoning with experimental probability	conducting trials of a game or experiment to determine experimental probabilities (*How Likely Is It?*); organizing data collected from experiments (*Variables and Patterns*; *Moving Straight Ahead*)	using data collected from samples of populations to determine experimental probabilities; developing techniques for simulating situations in order to collect and organize data (*Samples and Populations*)
understanding, determining, and reasoning with theoretical probability	analyzing simple games to determine theoretical probabilities (*How Likely Is It?*); interpreting fractions, decimals, and percents as a ratio of the number of desired outcomes to the number of all possible outcomes (*Bits and Pieces II*)	developing strategies for analyzing complex games or situations to determine theoretical probabilities (*Samples and Populations*); developing counting strategies to calculate theoretical probabilities (*Clever Counting*)
finding and reasoning with expected value	studying favorable outcomes, equally likely outcomes, and random outcomes (*How Likely Is It?*)	using expected values of favorable and unfavorable outcomes to make inferences and predictions; using expected values to make recommendations or to develop solutions to real-world problems (*Samples and Populations*; *Clever Counting*)

Technology

Connected Mathematics was developed with the belief that calculators should always be available and that students should decide when to use them. For this reason, we do not designate specific problems as "calculator problems."

Investigation 3 involves a simulation of Treasure Hunt, a computer game. The Treasure Hunt game offers students the opportunity to use technology to investigate a probability situation. This program can be downloaded from the Connected Mathematics home page (http://www.ns.msu.edu/CMP/cmp.html), or it can be obtained by sending ten dollars (to cover the cost of the disk, the documentation, and shipping and handling) to: Connected Education Technology, P.O. Box 1014, East Lansing, MI 48826. Please indicate whether you would like the Windows or Macintosh version.

Pacing Chart

This pacing chart gives estimates of the class time required for each investigation and assessment piece. Shaded rows indicate opportunities for assessment.

Investigations and Assessments	Class Time
1 Evaluating Games of Chance	3 days
2 Analyzing Number-Cube Games	2 days
Check-Up 1	$\frac{1}{2}$ day
3 Probability and Area	2 days
Quiz A	1 day
4 Analyzing Two-Stage Games	3 days
5 Expected Value	3 days
Check-Up 2	$\frac{1}{2}$ day
6 Carnival Games	3 days
Quiz B	1 day
7 Analyzing Sequences of Outcomes	3 days
Self-Assessment	Take home
Unit Test	1 day

What Do You Expect? Vocabulary

The following words and concepts are used in *What Do You Expect?* Concepts in the left column are those essential for student understanding of this and future units. The Descriptive Glossary gives descriptions of many of these words.

**Essential terms
developed in this unit**
counting tree
expected value, long-term average

**Terms developed
in previous units**
equally likely
event
experimental probability
fair game
outcome
probability
random
theoretical probability

Nonessential terms
payoff
Law of Large Numbers

Assessment Summary

Embedded Assessment

Opportunities for informal assessment of student progress are embedded throughout *What Do You Expect?* in the problems, the ACE questions, and the Mathematical Reflections. Suggestions for observing as students explore and discover mathematical ideas, for probing to guide their progress in developing concepts and skills, and for questioning to determine their level of understanding can be found in the Launch, Explore, or Summarize sections of all investigation problems. Some examples:

- Investigation 5, Problem 5.1 *Launch* (page 58a) suggests a process you can use to help your students understand the kinds of things they must consider when designing a simulation of a probability situation in order to generate experimental probabilities.

- Investigation 6, Problem 6.1 *Explore* (page 68b) suggests questions you can ask to assess your students' understanding of the concept of bias in an experimental situation.

- Investigation 1, Problem 1.3 *Summarize* (page 21g) suggests extension questions you can ask to assess your students' understanding of how to compute theoretical probabilities in a simple game of chance.

ACE Assignments

An ACE (Applications—Connections—Extensions) section appears at the end of each investigation. To help you assign ACE questions, a list of assignment choices is given in the margin next to the reduced student page for each problem. Each list indicates the ACE questions that students should be able to answer after they complete the problem.

Check-Ups

Two check-ups, which may be given after Investigations 2 and 5, are provided for use as quick quizzes or warm-up activities. The check-ups are designed for students to complete individually. You will find the check-ups and their answer keys in the Assessment Resources section.

Partner Quizzes

Two quizzes, which may be given after Investigations 3 and 6, are provided with *What Do You Expect?* The quizzes are designed to be completed by pairs of students with the opportunity for revision based on teacher feedback. You will find the quizzes and their answer keys in the Assessment Resources section. As an alternative to the quizzes provided, you can construct your own quizzes by combining questions from the Question Bank, these quizzes, and unassigned ACE questions.

Question Bank

A Question Bank provides questions you can use for homework, reviews, or quizzes. You will find the Question Bank and its answer key in the Assessment Resources section.

Notebook/Journal

Students should have notebooks to record and organize their work. Notebooks should include student journals and sections for vocabulary, homework, quizzes, and check-ups. In their journals, students can take notes, solve investigation problems, and record their ideas about Mathematical Reflections questions. Journals should be assessed for completeness rather than correctness; they should be seen as "safe" places where students can try out their thinking. A Notebook Checklist and a Self-Assessment are provided in the Assessment Resources section. The Notebook Checklist helps students organize their notebooks. The Self-Assessment guides students as they review their notebooks to determine which ideas they have mastered and which they still need to work on.

The Unit Test

The final assessment for *What Do You Expect?* is a unit test that focuses on three probability situations. Several questions are asked about each situation. Some of the questions check students' understanding of fundamental concepts; others are problem-solving questions that probe more deeply to assess how students are reasoning about what they know.

The Unit Project: The Carnival Game

What Do You Expect? also includes a unit project, the Carnival Game project. The project gives students an opportunity to apply what they have learned about probability and expected value in a real-world situation. Students will work in groups to design a game for a school carnival, and then submit a model of their game and a written report that, among other things, describes how the game is played and analyzes the expected payoff. The blackline masters describing the project and a guide for assessing the project are included in the Assessment Resources section. Samples of students' work, along with a teacher's comments about how each sample was assessed, will help you to evaluate your students' efforts on this project.

Introducing Your Students to *What Do You Expect?*

Several days before starting the unit, challenge students to find examples—from newspapers, magazines, radio, or television—of statements that give the likelihood, or probability, that something will happen. On the day you start the unit, let students present the examples they found. This introduction will set the tone for the kind of discussions that will take place in *What Do You Expect?*

When students have shared their examples, discuss the three situations that are posed on the opening page of the student edition. The point is not to answer questions, but to raise questions that students should continue to ask about new situations throughout the unit, such as the following:

What does it mean to say that the probability of a particular event happening is $\frac{3}{5}$?

How do you think the statements that are made in this article were determined?

What Do You Expect?

In the district finals, Nicky has just been fouled and is in a one-and-one free-throw situation. This means that she must make her first shot to try a second shot. Nicky's free-throw average is 60%. Is Nicky most likely to miss the first shot, to make the first shot and miss the second shot, or to make both shots?

Raymundo invented the Prime Number Multiplication game. Two 1-6 number cubes are rolled to get a product. Player A scores 10 points if the product is prime, and Player B scores 1 point if it is not prime. Raymundo thinks his game is fair because there are many more ways to roll a nonprime product than a prime product. Is his game a fair game?

Have you ever had to guess because you forgot to study for a quiz? If you take a five-question true-false quiz and guess on every question, what are your chances of getting every question right?

Probabilities can help you make decisions. For example, if the weather report says there is a 75% chance of rain, you might decide to carry an umbrella. If you know there is a 1 in 1,000,000 chance of winning the lottery, you might choose not to play. Probabilities can also help you predict what will happen over the long run. For example, if you and your friend flip a coin before each baseball game to determine who will be catcher, you can predict that you will be catcher for about half the games.

Many probability situations involve some kind of payoff—points scored in a game, money won in a lottery, or profit earned from a business venture. It is often useful to find the long-term average payoff, or the *expected value*, in situations like these. For example, when deciding whether to make an investment, a company might want to figure out how much it can expect to earn over the long run.

In this unit, you will look at questions involving probability and expected value, including the three questions on the opposite page.

What would you need to know to find the probability of a given outcome?

If the chances that a given outcome will happen are determined to be 60%, does this mean that out of every ten trials, the outcome will occur exactly six times?

These discussions will give you an idea of how familiar students are with the concepts from the grade 6 probability unit, *How Likely Is It?*

Mathematical Highlights

The Mathematical Highlights page provides information for students and for parents and other family members. It gives students a preview of the activities and problems in *What Do You Expect?* As they work through the unit, students can refer back to the Mathematical Highlights page to review what they have learned and to preview what is still to come. This page also tells students' families what mathematical ideas and activities will be covered as the class works through *What Do You Expect?*

Mathematical Highlights

In *What Do You Expect?* you will explore ways to deepen your understanding of basic probability concepts and learn about the expected value of chance situations. This unit will help you to

- Understand experimental and theoretical probabilities and the relationship between them;

- Further develop ways to identify the possible outcomes of an event;

- Understand the distinction between equally likely and non–equally likely events;

- Analyze situations that involve independent events and situations that involve dependent events;

- Develop a variety of strategies for analyzing probabilities, such as using lists, counting trees and area models;

- Determine the expected value of a chance situation; and

- Use probability and expected value to make decisions.

As you work on the problems in this unit, ask yourself questions about situations that involve analyzing probabilities: *What are the possible outcomes for the event(s) in this situation? Are they equally likely? Can I compute the theoretical probabilities or do I need to find experimental probabilities associated with the outcomes of the event(s)? If I'm exploring two or more events, are they independent or dependent events? In the context of games, how can I use expected value to help me determine whether a game is fair or unfair?*

The Investigations

The teaching materials for each investigation consist of three parts: an overview, student pages with teaching outlines, and detailed notes for teaching the investigation.

The overview of each investigation includes brief descriptions of the problems, the mathematical and problem-solving goals of the investigation, and a list of necessary materials.

Essential information for teaching the investigation is provided in the margins around the student pages. The "At a Glance" overviews are brief outlines of the Launch, Explore, and Summarize phases of each problem for reference as you work with the class. To help you assign homework, a list of "Assignment Choices" is provided next to each problem. Wherever space permits, answers to problems, follow-ups, ACE questions, and Mathematical Reflections appear next to the appropriate student pages.

The Teaching the Investigation section follows the student pages and is the heart of the Connected Mathematics curriculum. This section describes in detail the Launch, Explore, and Summarize phases for each problem. It includes all the information needed for teaching, along with suggestions for what you might say at key points in the teaching. Use this section to prepare lessons and as a guide for teaching investigations.

Assessment Resources

The Assessment Resources section contains blackline masters and answer keys for the check-ups, quizzes, the Question Bank, and the Unit Test. Blackline masters for the Notebook Checklist and the Self-Assessment are given. These instruments support student self-evaluation, an important aspect of assessment in the Connected Mathematics curriculum. The unit project appears at the end of the student text. A discussion of how one teacher assessed students' work on the project is included, along with sample pages of students' work. Samples of three students' responses to the Self-Assessment are also shown, along with a teacher's evaluation.

Blackline Masters

The Blackline Masters section includes masters for all labsheets and transparencies. Blackline masters of 10 by 10 grids, blank spinners, and grid paper are also provided.

Additional Practice

Practice pages for each investigation offer additional problems for students who need more practice with the basic concepts developed in the investigations as well as some continual review of earlier concepts.

Descriptive Glossary

The Descriptive Glossary provides descriptions and examples of the key concepts in *What Do You Expect?* These descriptions are not intended to be formal definitions, but are meant to give you an idea of how students might make sense of these important concepts.

Evaluating Games of Chance

Students' natural interest in exploring the fairness of games is highlighted in this investigation, in which students analyze several games of chance. These captivating games review the ideas that are developed in the grade 6 probability unit, *How Likely Is It?*

In Problem 1.1, What's in the Bucket?, the class gathers data to determine the probabilities of drawing blocks of various colors from a container. In the process, students review basic ideas about the concept of probability. In Problem 1.2, Matching Colors, students collect data about a game played with a spinner to find the associated experimental probabilities. Then, they compute theoretical probabilities and analyze whether the game is a fair game. In Problem 1.3, Making Purple, students investigate experimental and theoretical probabilities for another spinner game. While continuing to review the concept of probability, they also think about questions that hint at the concept of expected value. Problem 1.4, Making Counting Trees, formally introduces students to a visual method of computing theoretical probabilities.

Mathematical and Problem-Solving Goals

- *To review and develop a deeper understanding of experimental and theoretical probabilities and the relationship between them*

- *To review and extend methods of finding experimental probabilities*

- *To review and extend methods of finding theoretical probabilities, including making an organized list, or counting tree, of all possible outcomes*

- *To review the distinction between equally likely and non–equally likely outcomes*

- *To determine whether a game is fair or unfair*

- *To make unfair games fair by informally applying the concept of expected value*

Materials		
Problem	**For students**	**For the teacher**
All	Graphing calculators	Transparencies 1.1 to 1.4 (optional)
1.1		Opaque container filled with 4 blue, 8 yellow, and 12 red blocks (substitute other colors or objects if necessary); 16 additional blue blocks
1.2	Labsheet 1.2 (1 per pair), paper clips or bobby pins (for spinners; 1 per pair)	Transparency of Labsheet 1.2 (optional)
1.3	Labsheet 1.3 (1 per pair), paper clips or bobby pins (for spinners; 2 per pair)	Transparency of Labsheet 1.3 (optional)

Student Pages 5–21   Teaching the Investigation 21a–21l

Evaluating Games of Chance

In this investigation, you will explore several games involving chance. In each situation, you are asked to determine the chance, or *probability*, that certain outcomes will occur. In some situations, you will also be asked to determine whether a particular game is fair. What do you think it means for a game to be fair?

1.1 What's in the Bucket?

One day, Ms. MacAfee brought a mysterious bucket to class. She did not show her students what was in the bucket, but she told them that it contained blue, yellow, and red blocks. She asked if they could predict, without emptying the bucket, the fraction of the blocks that were blue, the fraction that were yellow, and the fraction that were red.

The class conducted an experiment to help them make their predictions. Each student randomly selected a block from the bucket, and the result was recorded on the board. After each draw, the block was returned to the bucket before the next student selected a block. In this problem, your class will conduct a similar experiment.

What's in the Bucket?

At a Glance

Grouping: Whole Class, then Pairs

Launch

- Show the class the container, and tell them that it contains different colors of blocks.
- Ask students how they might predict how many blocks of each color are in the container.
- Talk about conducting an experiment to determine the number of blocks of each color.
- As a class, collect data by having each student draw a block, record its color, and return it.

Explore

- Have the class count the blocks of each color and then answer parts D and E.

Summarize

- Have students share their answers to the problem, and review basic ideas about experimental and theoretical probabilities.
- Talk about the follow-up.

Assignment Choices

ACE question 18

1.2

Matching Colors

Launch

- Explain that students will be analyzing April and Tioko's spinner game.

- Demonstrate how to take one turn (two spins).

- Distribute Labsheet 1.2 and a paper clip to each pair of students.

Explore

- Circulate as pairs collect their data.

Summarize

- Discuss the students' findings.

- As a class, combine all the data collected and use the experimental probabilities to make predictions.

- Talk about how to find the theoretical probabilities and how to determine whether the game is fair.

Problem 1.1

Your teacher has prepared a bucket identical to Ms. MacAfee's. One at a time, you and each of your classmates will select a block from the bucket, record the result, and return the block to the bucket.

A. How many blocks drawn by your class were blue? How many were yellow? How many were red?

B. Which color block—blue, yellow, or red—do you think there are the greatest number of in the bucket? Which color block do you think there are the least number of?

C. Based on your experimental data, predict the fraction of blocks in the bucket that are blue, that are yellow, and that are red.

D. After your teacher shows you the blocks in the bucket, find the fraction of blue blocks, the fraction of yellow blocks, and the fraction of red blocks.

E. How do the fractions of blocks that are blue, yellow, and red compare to the fractions of blue, yellow, and red blocks drawn during the experiment?

▇ Problem 1.1 Follow-Up

1. a. Is each block *equally likely* to be selected from the bucket? That is, does each block have the same chance of being selected? Explain your reasoning.

    b. Is each color equally likely to be selected? Explain your reasoning.

2. What is the probability of drawing a white block from the bucket?

3. How many blue blocks need to be added to the bucket for the probability of drawing a blue block to be $\frac{1}{2}$?

1.2 Matching Colors

April and Tioko invented a two-player spinner game called Match/No-Match. A player spins this spinner twice on his or her turn. If both spins land on the same color (a match), Player A scores. If the two spins land on different colors (a no-match), Player B scores. Since there are two matching combinations—blue/blue and yellow/yellow—they decided that Player A should score only 1 point for a match and Player B should score 2 points for a no-match.

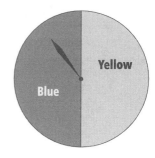

ACE questions 1–7 and unassigned choices from earlier problems

Answers to Problem 1.1

A. Answers will vary.

B. greatest: red; least: blue

C. Answers should be close to $\frac{1}{6}$ for blue, $\frac{1}{3}$ for yellow, and $\frac{1}{2}$ for red.

D. blue: $\frac{4}{24}$ or $\frac{1}{6}$, yellow: $\frac{8}{24}$ or $\frac{1}{3}$, red: $\frac{12}{24}$ or $\frac{1}{2}$

E. The fractions should be reasonably close.

Answers to Problem 1.1 Follow-Up

See page 21i.

Problem 1.2

Play the Match/No-Match game with a partner. Take a total of 24 turns (12 turns for each player). For each turn, record the color pair on Labsheet 1.2, and award points to the appropriate player.

A. Use the results you collected to find the *experimental probabilities* of a match and a no-match. The experimental probability of a match is

$$P(match) = \frac{\text{number of turns that are matches}}{\text{total number of turns}}$$

The experimental probability of a no-match is

$$P(no\text{-}match) = \frac{\text{number of turns that are no-matches}}{\text{total number of turns}}$$

B. List all the possible **outcomes** of a turn (two spins). Write the outcomes as pairs of the form *color on first spin / color on second spin*, such as blue/blue. Use your list to determine the *theoretical probabilities* of a match and a no-match. Since all the outcomes are equally likely, the theoretical probability of a match is

$$P(match) = \frac{\text{number of outcomes that are matches}}{\text{number of possible outcomes}}$$

The theoretical probability of a no-match is

$$P(no\text{-}match) = \frac{\text{number of outcomes that are no-matches}}{\text{number of possible outcomes}}$$

C. How do your results for parts A and B compare?

D. Is Match/No-Match a **fair game**? If you think the game is fair, explain why. If you think it is not fair, explain how the rules could be changed to make it fair.

■ Problem 1.2 Follow-Up

1. Are a match and a no-match equally likely? Explain your reasoning.

2. In 100 turns of the Match/No-Match game, how many times would you expect each of the following to occur?

  a. two yellows

  b. two blues

  c. one yellow and one blue

  d. at least one yellow

Answers to Problem 1.2

A. Answers will vary. In one game played by two students, there were 13 matches and 11 no-matches, making $P(match) = \frac{13}{24}$ and $P(no\text{-}match) = \frac{11}{24}$.

B. Of the four possible outcomes—blue/blue, blue/yellow, yellow/blue, and yellow/yellow—two are matches and two are no-matches. The theoretical probability of a match is $\frac{2}{4}$ or $\frac{1}{2}$, and the theoretical probability of a no-match is $\frac{2}{4}$ or $\frac{1}{2}$.

C. The results should be close.

D. The game is not fair, as the two events—spinning a match and spinning a no-match— are equally likely but the players do not receive the same number of points for each event. Scoring 1 point for a match and 1 point for a no-match would make it fair.

Answers to Problem 1.2 Follow-Up

1, 2.　　See page 21i.

Making Purple

At a Glance

Grouping:
Pairs

Launch

■ Demonstrate how to play the two-spinner game.

■ Ask the class whether they think the game is fair.

■ Distribute Labsheet 1.3 and two paper clips to each pair, and have them explore the problem.

Explore

■ Circulate as pairs work, helping those who are having difficulty analyzing the game.

Summarize

■ Have students share their strategies for finding the experimental and theoretical probabilities.

■ Arrange students in small groups to explore the follow-up.

■ Talk about the follow-up.

■ Pose additional questions to check students' understanding.

Assignment Choices

ACE questions 8, 10, 11, 13, 15, and unassigned choices from earlier problems

3. a. Look at your results on Labsheet 1.2. If you had stopped after one turn, what would have been the experimental probability of a match? If you had stopped after two turns, what would have been the experimental probability of a match? If you had stopped after three turns, what would have been the experimental probability of a match? Continue to find the experimental probabilities through 24 turns. Record your results in a table.

b. Plot your data from part a on a coordinate grid similar to the one below.

c. What do you think your graph would look like if you had taken 30 turns? 50 turns? 100 turns? 1000 turns?

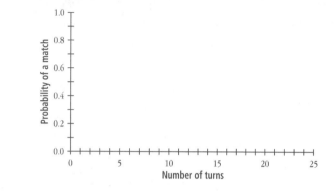

1.3 Making Purple

The most popular game at the school carnival is a spinner game called Making Purple. To play the game, a player spins each of the spinners below once. If the player gets red on spinner A and blue on spinner B, the player wins, because red and blue together make purple.

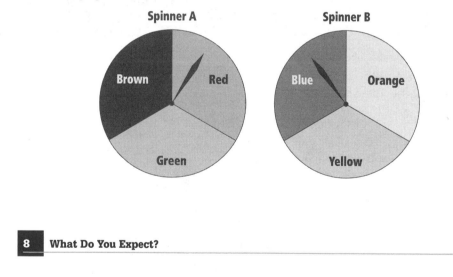

3. See page 21i.

Problem 1.3

A. Play Making Purple 50 times, and record the results on Labsheet 1.3. Based on your results, what is the experimental probability that a player will "make purple" on any single turn?

B. Plot the experimental probability of making purple you would have found if you had stopped after 5 turns, 10 turns, 15 turns, and so on, up to 50 turns.

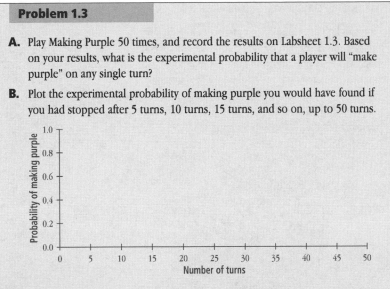

C. What do you think your graph would look like if you had taken 100 turns? 200 turns? 1000 turns?

D. List the possible outcomes for a turn. Write the outcomes as pairs of the form *color on spinner A/color on spinner B*. Are the outcomes equally likely? Explain why or why not.

E. What is the theoretical probability that a player will make purple on a turn?

F. How does the experimental probability of making purple compare with the theoretical probability of making purple? Explain.

▨ Problem 1.3 Follow-Up

1. If 36 people play this game, how many would you expect to win? Explain how you got your answer.

2. Tickets at the school carnival cost 50¢ each. It takes four tickets to play the Making Purple game. The prizes awarded to the winners cost the school $5 each. Suppose 36 people play the game.

   a. How much money will the school take in from this game?

   b. How much money would you expect the school to pay out in prizes?

   c. How much profit would you expect the school to make from this game?

Answers to Problem 1.3

A. Data will vary. Each pair's data should show about 11% of the spins making purple.

B. See page 21j.

C. The graph would fluctuate less and less as the number of trials increased, and the probability would hover around 0.11.

D. The possible outcomes are brown/blue, brown/orange, brown/yellow, green/blue, green/orange, green/yellow, red/blue, red/orange, and red/yellow. The outcomes are equally likely, as all sections on the spinners are the same size.

E. $P(\text{purple}) = \frac{1}{9}$

F. See page 21j.

Answers to Problem 1.3 Follow-Up

See page 21k.

Making Counting Trees

Grouping: Individuals, then Small Groups

Launch

- Use the example in the student edition to illustrate how to make a counting tree.

- Talk about how to read a counting tree.

- Have students work individually to make their counting trees, then gather in groups to share results and to answer the questions.

Explore

- Assist students who need help getting started.

- Have groups move on to the follow-up when they finish the problem.

Summarize

- Ask several students to share their counting trees.

- Verify that the class can read a counting tree.

- Review the follow-up questions.

Assignment Choices

ACE questions 9, 12, 14, 16, 17, 19, 20, and unassigned choices from earlier problems

1.4 Making Counting Trees

You can find all the possible outcomes of a situation by making an organized list. Creating a **counting tree** can help you make sure you find all the possibilities. April used a counting tree to show all the possible outcomes for the Match/No-Match game (from Problem 1.2). First, she listed the equally likely outcomes of the first spin as shown in the tree at right below.

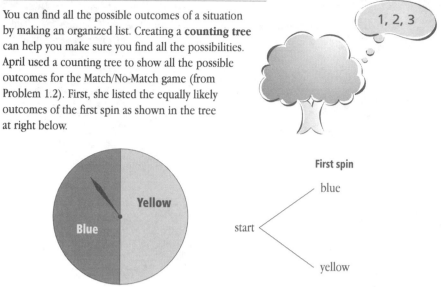

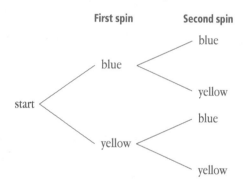

A turn consists of two spins, so from each of the possible results of the first spin, April drew two branches and labeled them to show the possible results of the second spin.

By following the paths from left to right, April can read all the possible outcomes of a turn. For example, she can follow the upper branch from start to blue, and then from there follow the upper branch to blue. This path represents the outcome blue/blue.

Answers to Problem 1.4

A.

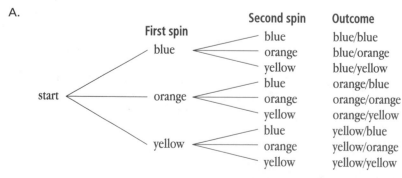

The column to the right of the tree below lists the possible outcomes.

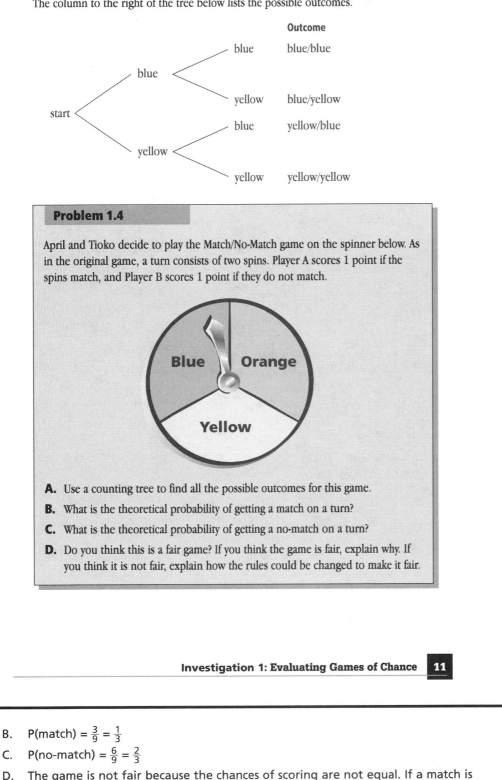

Outcome

blue — blue/blue

blue

yellow — blue/yellow

start

blue — yellow/blue

yellow

yellow — yellow/yellow

Problem 1.4

April and Tioko decide to play the Match/No-Match game on the spinner below. As in the original game, a turn consists of two spins. Player A scores 1 point if the spins match, and Player B scores 1 point if they do not match.

A. Use a counting tree to find all the possible outcomes for this game.

B. What is the theoretical probability of getting a match on a turn?

C. What is the theoretical probability of getting a no-match on a turn?

D. Do you think this is a fair game? If you think the game is fair, explain why. If you think it is not fair, explain how the rules could be changed to make it fair.

B. P(match) = $\frac{3}{9}$ = $\frac{1}{3}$

C. P(no-match) = $\frac{6}{9}$ = $\frac{2}{3}$

D. The game is not fair because the chances of scoring are not equal. If a match is awarded 2 points rather than 1, the expected number of points scored will be the same for both players and the game will be fair.

■ **Problem 1.4 Follow-Up**

1. a. Find all the possible outcomes for the Making Purple game in Problem 1.3 by creating a counting tree.

b. Use your counting tree to find the theoretical probability of making purple on a turn.

c. How does the theoretical probability you found by using a counting tree compare with the theoretical probability you found in Problem 1.3?

2. Shondra played a game with a spinner and a coin. For each turn, she spun the spinner once and tossed the coin once. For example, one possible outcome would be blue/head.

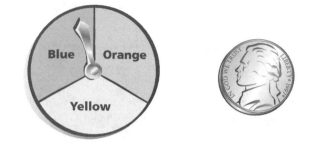

a. Create a counting tree to find all the possible outcomes of a turn in Shondra's game.

b. Are all the outcomes equally likely? Explain why or why not.

c. What is the probability that Shondra will spin blue and toss a head on a turn?

Answers to Problem 1.4 Follow-Up

1. a. See page 21k.

   b. P(purple) = $\frac{1}{9}$

   c. The probabilities are the same.

2. a. See page 21k.

   b. The outcomes are all equally likely because each has the same probability of occurring, $\frac{1}{6}$.

   c. P(blue/head) = $\frac{1}{6}$

As you work on these ACE questions, use your calculator whenever you need it.

Applications

In 1–5, decide whether the possible resulting events are equally likely, and briefly explain your answer.

Action	Possible resulting events
1. You roll a number cube.	You roll an even number, or you roll an odd number.
2. A baby is born.	The baby is left-handed, or the baby is right-handed.
3. You toss a marshmallow.	The marshmallow lands on its end, or the marshmallow lands on its side.
4. You draw a card from a standard deck of 52 playing cards with no jokers.	The card is a heart, the card is a club, the card is a diamond, or the card is a spade.
5. You toss a coin three times.	You get three heads, you get two heads and a tail, you get a head and two tails, or you get three tails.

Answers

Applications

1. The events are equally likely, as there are three ways to roll an even number (2, 4, and 6) and three ways to roll an odd number (1, 3, and 5), and each number is equally likely.

2. The events are probably not equally likely, as handedness is not evenly distributed and probably depends on genetics and social influence.

3. The events are probably not equally likely; explanations will vary. (Note: If students have not explored this question in the grade 6 unit *How Likely Is It?* you might have them try this as an experiment.)

4. The events are equally likely, as there are 13 cards of each suit in a deck.

5. The events are not equally likely, as there is only one way to get three heads (HHH), three ways to get two heads (HHT, HTH, and THH), three ways to get two tails (TTH, THT, and HTT), and one way to get three tails (TTT).

6. See below right.

6. The probability of an event is a number between 0 and 1. The greater the probability, the greater the chances the event will happen. If an event is impossible, the probability that it will occur is 0, or 0%. If an event is certain to happen, the probability that it will occur is 1, or 100%.

Copy the number line below. Place the letter of each event below on the number line at the spot that best describes its probability.

impossible   certain

```
|---+---+---+---+---+---+---+---+---+---|
0.0                    0.5                    1.0
```

a. You will get a head when you toss a coin.

b. You can run 20 miles in one hour.

c. You will roll a 6 on a number cube.

d. It will snow in Minnesota this winter.

e. The sun will rise tomorrow.

f. You will toss a coin twice and get two heads.

g. You will toss a coin twice and get at least one head.

h. You will listen to a CD today.

i. You will spin the spinner shown below once, and it will land on red.

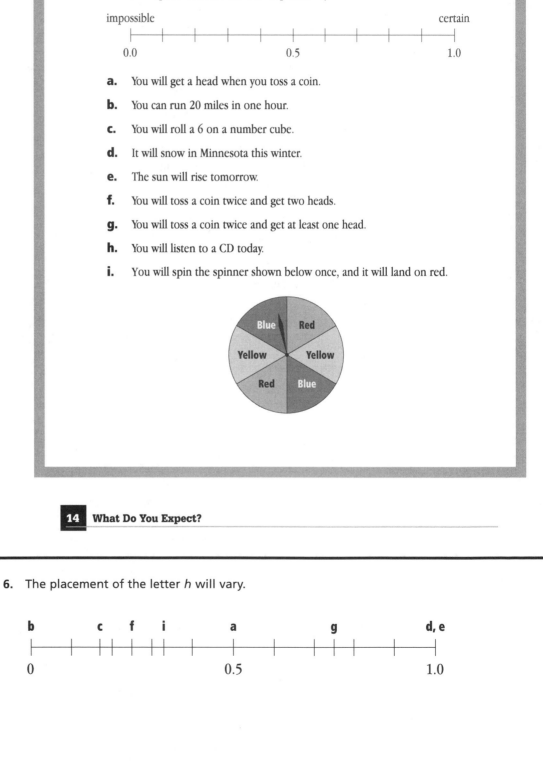

6. The placement of the letter *h* will vary.

```
b           c    f    i          a              g          d, e
|---+---++---+---++---+---+---+---+---+---|
0                      0.5                    1.0
```

7. Lori's little sister Lulu tore the labels from ten cans of vegetables. Now all of the cans look exactly the same. Lori knows that three of the cans contain corn, two contain spinach, four contain beans, and one contains tomatoes. Lori picks a can at random and opens it.

   a. What is the probability that the can contains corn?

   b. What is the probability that the can contains beans?

   c. What is the probability that the can does *not* contain spinach?

   d. What is the probability that the can contains beans or tomatoes?

   e. Is it equally likely that any one of the vegetables is in the can? Explain.

8. If a tack is dropped on the floor, there are two possible outcomes: the tack lands on its side (point down), or the tack lands on its head (point up). The probability that a tack will land point up or point down can be determined by experimenting. Kalifa tossed a tack 100 times and recorded the results in the table below.

point down   point up

Outcome	Number of times it occurs
Tack lands point up	58
Tack lands point down	42

   a. If you dropped Kalifa's tack once, what is the probability that it would land point up? What is the probability that it would land point down?

   b. If you dropped Kalifa's tack 500 times, how many times would you expect it to land point up?

   c. Is it equally likely that the tack will land point up or point down? Explain.

   d. Is it possible to determine theoretical probabilities for this situation? Why or why not?

7a. $\frac{3}{10}$ or 0.3

7b. $\frac{4}{10}$ or 0.4

7c. $\frac{8}{10}$ or 0.8

7d. $\frac{5}{10}$ or 0.5

7e. no; The probabilities that the can contains each vegetable are not the same, so the vegetables are not equally likely to be in the can.

8a. P(tack will land point up) = $\frac{58}{100}$, 0.58, or 58%; P(tack will land point down) = $\frac{42}{100}$, 0.42, or 42%

8b. This tack could be expected to land point up 58% of the 500 times, or about 290 times.

8c. Based on the experimental probabilities given, the two outcomes are probably not equally likely. However, we cannot be certain without computing theoretical probabilities or conducting a very large number of trials.

8d. We cannot figure out the theoretical probabilities for this experiment (though a theoretical physicist might be able to do so!) because it is too complex.

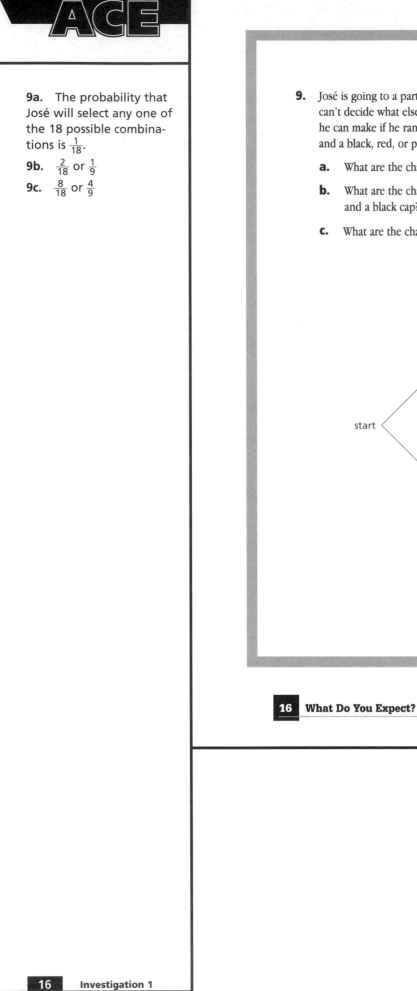

9a. The probability that José will select any one of the 18 possible combinations is $\frac{1}{18}$.

9b. $\frac{2}{18}$ or $\frac{1}{9}$

9c. $\frac{8}{18}$ or $\frac{4}{9}$

9. José is going to a party. He has decided to wear his jeans and a sweater, but he can't decide what else to wear. The counting tree below shows the possible outfits he can make if he randomly selects sneakers or loafers; blue, red, or brown socks; and a black, red, or plaid cap.

a. What are the chances that José will wear loafers, blue socks, and a plaid cap?

b. What are the chances that José will wear sneakers, either red or blue socks, and a black cap?

c. What are the chances that José will wear neither red socks nor a red cap?

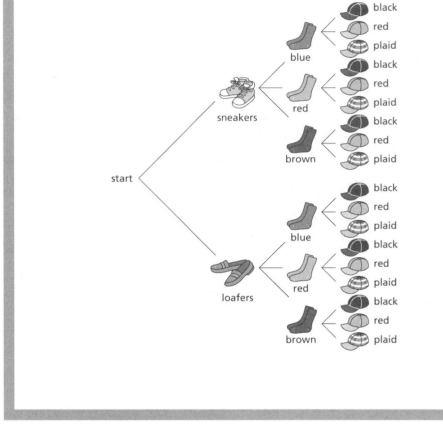

10. Tino and Kim are playing a game with two pennies. The players take turns tossing both pennies. If the pennies match, Tino scores 1 point. If they don't match, Kim scores 1 point.

   a. Is this a fair game? Explain.

   b. How does this game compare to the Match/No-Match game in Problem 1.2?

   c. Kim suggests playing the game with three pennies instead of two. The rules would be the same—Tino would get a point if the three pennies matched, and Kim would get a point if they didn't all match. Is this a fair game? Why or why not?

11. In the Gee Whiz Everyone Wins! television game show, members of the studio audience draw a block randomly from the bucket shown at right. If a blue block is drawn, the contestant wins $5. If a red block is drawn, the contestant wins $10. If the yellow block is drawn, the contestant wins $50. The block is replaced after each draw.

   a. What is the probability of drawing each color?

   b. If 24 contestants draw a block from the bucket, how much money can the game show expect to pay out?

12. At the school carnival, the Math Club is running a coin-toss game. It costs four 50¢ tickets to play the game. A player tosses two coins. If the coins match, the player wins a prize. Each prize costs the club $5. Can the club expect to make a profit on this game? If so, how much? If not, explain why.

13. Tioko and Dione are using the spinners from the Making Purple game to play a two-person game. They take turns spinning the two spinners. If the colors on the two spinners make purple, Dione scores. If they do not make purple, Tioko scores. For this to be a fair game, how many points should Dione score when the spinners make purple, and how many points should Tioko score when they do not make purple?

13. Possible answer: Dione could score 8 points for making purple, and Tioko could score 1 point for any other combination. In a game of 9 spins, for example, Dione can expect to make purple $\frac{1}{9}$ of the time (1 time) and receive 8 points. Tioko can expect to not make purple $\frac{8}{9}$ of the time (8 times) and also receive 8 points, making it a fair game.

10a. Yes, this is a fair game. Of the four possible outcomes—HH, TT, HT, and TH—there are two ways for the pennies to match and two ways for them not to match.

10b. The results of this game are similar to those of Match/No-Match. The outcomes in that game are blue/blue, yellow/yellow, yellow/blue, and blue/yellow. In each individual spin, blue and yellow are equally likely. In the toss of a coin, a head and a tail are equally likely.

10c. This is not a fair game. Of the eight possible outcomes—HHH, HHT, HTH, THH, TTH, THT, HTT, and TTT—two are matches and six are not matches.

11a. P(red) = $\frac{2}{6}$, P(blue) = $\frac{3}{6}$, P(yellow) = $\frac{1}{6}$

11b. Of 24 contestants, the game show could expect 12 to draw blue (50% of 24), 8 to draw red (33% of 24), and 4 to draw yellow (17% of 24), an expected payout of $5(12) + $10(8) + $50(4) = $340.

12. The club cannot expect to make a profit over the long run. Possible explanation: Suppose 100 people play the game. Each player pays $2 to play, giving the club $200. The club can expect to pay out about half of the time (since half of the possible outcomes result in a match), so about 50 contestants will win. If 50 people win $5 each, the club will be paying out $250—an overall loss of $50, or about 50¢ per player.

14a. See below right.

14b. P(purple) = $\frac{1}{6}$

Connections

15a. See below right.

15b. $\frac{5}{6}$ or 83%

15c. $\frac{7}{8}$ or 87.5%

14. Suppose the spinners for the Making Purple game were changed to the following.

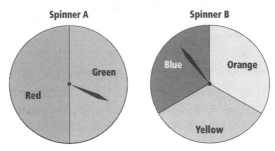

Spinner A

Spinner B

a. Make a counting tree, and list all the possible outcomes for this game.

b. Find the theoretical probability of making purple on a turn.

Connections

15. A dart is thrown at random at each of the dartboards below.

Board 1   Board 2   Board 3

a. For each dartboard, what is the probability that a dart will land in a region marked A? A region marked B? A region marked C?

b. For board 1, what is the probability that a dart will land in a region marked A or B?

c. For board 2, what is the probability that a dart will *not* land in region C?

14a.

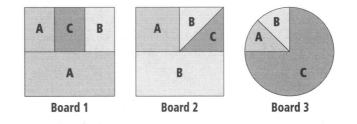

	Region A	Region B	Region C
Board 1	$\frac{4}{6}$ or 67%	$\frac{1}{6}$ or 17%	$\frac{1}{6}$ or 17%
Board 2	$\frac{1}{4}$ or 25%	$\frac{5}{8}$ or 62.5%	$\frac{1}{8}$ or 12.5%
Board 3	$\frac{1}{8}$ or 12.5%	$\frac{1}{8}$ or 12.5%	$\frac{3}{4}$ or 75%

15a.

16. A dartboard is divided into four regions, A, B, C, and D. The probability that a randomly thrown dart will land in region A is 40%. The probabilities that the dart will land in region B, region C, or region D are all equal.

   a. What is the probability that a dart will land in a region other than A?

   b. Make a square dartboard that meets the given conditions.

   c. Make a circular dartboard that meets the given conditions.

17. Jason spins the spinner below several times and tallies the results in a table.

   a. How many times did Jason spin the spinner?

   b. What percent of the spins landed in the blue region? In the yellow region?

   c. According to the theoretical probabilities, what percent of the spins should land in the blue region? In the yellow region?

   d. Compare the experimental probability of the spinner landing in each region with the theoretical probability. If the probabilities are different, explain why.

Extensions

18. A bucket contains 60 marbles—some red, some blue, and some white. The probability of drawing a red marble is 35%, and the probability of drawing a blue marble is 25%. How many marbles of each color are in the bucket?

16a. 60%

16b. See below left.

16c. See below left.

17a. 25 times

17b. blue: 36%; yellow: 64%

17c. Theoretically, the spinner should land on blue 25% of the time and yellow 75% of the time.

17d. The experimental and the theoretical probabilities differ. Possible explanation: A theoretical probability, if based on many trials, tells you about what to expect, but 25 is not a great number of spins. With more spins, the experimental probabilities would probably be closer to the theoretical probabilities.

Extensions

18. *red:* 35% of 60 is 21 marbles; *blue:* 25% of 60 is 15 marbles; *white:* 60 − 36 is 24 marbles

---

16b. Possible answers (region A must occupy 40% and regions B, C, and D must each occupy 20%):

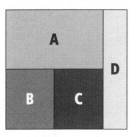 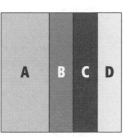

16c. Possible answer:

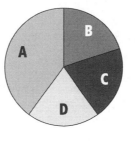

19. Five draws out of 14 is about 36%, and 36% of 72 blocks is about 26 blocks. However, 14 draws is not enough to make a good prediction of the number of blue blocks in the bucket.

20a. See page 21l.

20b. Six of the 18 possible outcomes consist of blocks of the same color, a probability of $\frac{6}{18}$ or $\frac{1}{3}$.

20c. The school could not expect to make money. Possible explanation: For 18 players, the school would take in $18 and could expect to pay out $3 to each of 6 players, making it a fair game with an expected profit of $0.

19. Hannah's teacher brought in a bucket containing 72 blocks—some red, some yellow, and some blue. Hannah wanted to try to figure out how many of the blocks were blue without emptying the bucket. She drew a block from the bucket, recorded its color, and then replaced it. She did this 14 times. Of her 14 draws, 5 were blue. Based on Hannah's experiment, how many of the blocks are blue? Explain your answer.

20. All the winners from the Gee Whiz Everyone Wins! game show get an opportunity to compete for a bonus prize. Each contestant draws one block at random from each of the buckets shown below. If the blocks are the same color, the contestant wins a prize.

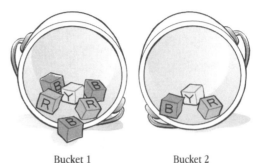

Bucket 1   Bucket 2

a. List all the possible outcomes when a player randomly draws one block from each bucket.

b. What is the probability that a contestant will draw two blocks of the same color?

c. Natasha wants to use a similar game at the school carnival. Contestants would pay two 50¢ tickets to play and would win a prize worth $3 for a match. Could the school expect to make money from this game? Explain.

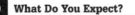

Mathematical Reflections

In this investigation, you explored games of chance. Working on the problems gave you an opportunity to review ideas about experimental probability and theoretical probability. These questions will help you summarize what you have learned:

1 **a.** Write a brief description of experimental probability.

 b. Describe a strategy you have used to find experimental probabilities.

2 **a.** Write a brief description of theoretical probability.

 b. Describe strategies you have used to find theoretical probabilities.

3 What does it mean for two or more events to be equally likely? Give examples of events that are equally likely.

Think about your answers to these questions, discuss your ideas with other students and your teacher, and then write a summary of your findings in your journal.

Tips for the Linguistically Diverse Classroom

Diagram Code The Diagram Code technique is described in detail in *Getting to Know Connected Mathematics*. Students use a minimal number of words and drawings, diagrams, or symbols to respond to questions that require writing. Example: Question 3—A student might answer this question by drawing the head and the tail of a coin and labeling the drawing *Same chance*.

Possible Answers

1a. An experimental probability is a probability based on data from conducting an experiment. If the experiment is conducted several times, you are likely to get several different experimental probabilities. However, if each experiment involves a large number of trials, the experimental probabilities will be very close to each other.

1b. We have found experimental probabilities by conducting many trials and then dividing the number of times a desired outcome occurred by the number of trials.

2a. A theoretical probability is what we can expect to happen if we do an experiment lots of times. We find theoretical probabilities by using math to analyze the situation rather than by experimenting.

2b. We made counting trees to list all the possible outcomes. Sometimes we just made lists by thinking about the possible outcomes.

3. Two or more events are equally likely if they have the same chance of occuring. For example, if I roll a number cube, the events of rolling 1, 2, 3, 4, 5, or 6 are all equally likely. If I toss a coin, the events of getting a head or a tail are equally likely.

TEACHING THE INVESTIGATION

1.1 • What's in the Bucket?

This problem offers students a review of some of the basic ideas about probability.

For the Teacher: Collecting Examples of Probability

Many examples of probability and expected value can be found in news-papers and magazines. As students progress through this unit, you might encourage them to bring any examples they find to school to share with the class. Another project you might conduct at some point during this unit is to have students investigate whether their state (or a neighboring state) has a lottery and to find out as much as they can about the cost of playing, the probabilities of winning, and the payoffs.

Launch

Read the story of Ms. MacAfee, or simply tell the class that you have put some blue, yellow, and red blocks into a container. Discuss with the class their ideas about the probability that a block drawn from the container will be a given color.

> I am going to thoroughly mix the blocks in this bucket. Now, if I call on someone to draw a block from the bucket—without looking into it— what is the probability that the person will draw a red block? A blue block? A yellow block?

Make sure students realize that although they could guess, they do not have enough information to make a prediction.

> If we want to do better than just guess, how could we gather some data to help us predict these probabilities?

From their previous work with probability, students should be able to suggest that they could conduct an experiment. They could draw blocks from the container and record their results.

> What kinds of things do we need to be careful about when we conduct our experiment?

Several ideas should emerge in this conversation. Each block drawn must be returned to the container so that the contents of the container do not change. The blocks must be mixed each time so that each has the same chance of being drawn. The results must be carefully recorded. Finally, the experiment must be repeated often enough that the class feels they have enough data to predict the probabilities with confidence.

With the class, read through the questions in the problem so that they all know what to be thinking about as they conduct the experiment.

> Notice that when we finish our experiment, we will look at the contents of the bucket to see how close our predictions are to what is actually in the bucket. Remember, though, that in real life we often need to conduct experiments to make predictions for situations in which there is no obvious way to analyze the situations theoretically.

As a class, gather the data, allowing at least one draw per student. You may want to have each student draw twice to make the point that we need to gather enough experimental data to have confidence in our estimate.

For the Teacher: Law of Large Numbers

The Law of Large Numbers tells us that as we gather more and more data—conduct more and more trials—the probabilities drawn from the experimental data should grow closer to the actual probabilities. This idea is difficult for students to grasp; they need time to experiment to develop an understanding of this concept. As you work with the class, talk about the need for many trials in conducting an experiment to find experimental probabilities. They will encounter this idea again in Problems 1.2 and 1.3.

Explore

Let students work in pairs or small groups on the problem and follow-up.

As they work with the data, ask questions about what they are discovering.

> What fraction of the blocks do you think are red? Blue? Yellow? How did you make your estimates?

> Is each *block* equally likely to be drawn? Why?

> Is each *color* equally likely to be drawn? Why?

Once students have analyzed their data, have them count the number of blocks of each color in the container so they can answer parts D and E.

Summarize

Have students share their responses to the questions and their explanations. Use this opportunity to review basic ideas about experimental and theoretical probabilities.

> What is an experimental probability? How can you find an experimental probability?

An *experimental probability* is a probability found by conducting an experiment and recording the number of trials and the results of each trial. To compute an experimental probability, a ratio is formed from the number of favorable trials (the number of times the outcome in which we are interested occurred) and the total number of trials:

$$P(\text{favorable outcome}) = \frac{\text{number of favorable outcomes}}{\text{number of trials}}$$

An experimental probability is used to make predictions about what will happen in the long run—in this case, if we continue to draw blocks from the container.

Review the follow-up questions with the class, continuing to discuss basic ideas about probability.

> What is the smallest number that can be a probability? *(0)* Give an example of an event with a probability of 0, and tell what it means. *(Drawing a purple block from the bucket has a probability of 0 because there are no purple blocks in the bucket. A probability of 0 means that the event is impossible.)*

> What is the greatest number that a probability can be? *(1)* Give an example of an event with a probability of 1, and explain what it means. *(Drawing a red, yellow, or blue block from our bucket has a probability of 1; if we draw a block, it must be one of these three colors. The probability that the sun will rise in the east and set in the west has a probability of 1. An event with a probability of 1 is certain to happen.)*

> Are the *individual blocks* in our bucket equally likely to be drawn? *(yes, provided that we mix them thoroughly)*

> Are the *colors* in our bucket equally likely to be chosen? How do you know? *(No; there are more reds than yellows and more yellows than blues. We know this because we drew many times and the fractions we found for each color are different. Red was drawn most often, and blue was drawn least often.)*

> When we counted the number of blocks of each color in the bucket, what kind of probability statements could we make? *(The fractions of actual number of blocks of each color over the total number of blocks in the container are the theoretical probabilities of drawing those colors.)*

A theoretical probability can be written as a ratio:

$$P(\text{drawing a red block}) = \frac{\text{number of red blocks}}{\text{total number of blocks}}$$

Ask the class to share their answers to follow-up question 3 and to explain their reasoning. Call on students until you are sure all ideas have been shared. Then, help them test their answers by adding the number of blue blocks they called for and analyzing the contents of the container. (You will need to add a total of 16 blue blocks, at which point the container will hold 20 blue blocks to equal the 20 that are yellow and red.)

1.2 • Matching Colors

In this problem, students analyze a game played with a spinner and review the idea of a fair game of chance.

Launch

Tell students that they will be analyzing April and Tioko's spinner game to decide whether it is fair. Describe the game, and demonstrate how to take one turn (by spinning the spinner twice), using a transparency of Labsheet 1.2 if possible. Place the point of a sharpened pencil or a pen through the rounded end of a bobby pin or paper clip and on the center of the spinner. Flick the bobby pin with your finger. Record the results. For example:

Turn number	Result	Player A's score	Player B's score
1	yellow/blue		2

> Who gets points for this turn? What is the payoff? *(If the two spins land on the same color, Player A scores 1 point. If the spins do not match, Player B scores 2 points.)*
>
> Is this a fair game? Why or why not?

Let students offer conjectures, but don't confirm or refute them at this time. This idea will be revisited in the summary of the problem.

Distribute Labsheet 1.2 and a paper clip or bobby pin to each pair of students. You may want to read the entire problem with the class to make sure they understand what they are to do.

> We want the results of our spins to be *random*—that is, we do not want anything about the way we spin the spinners to bias the results. What sorts of things might bias our results? *(slanted desktops, creased paper, always starting with the pointer in the same section, and so on)*

Explore

Have students work in pairs to collect the data, with each partner taking 12 turns. Once students have found experimental and theoretical probabilities and compared them, have them work on the follow-up questions.

Summarize

Discuss the students' data and their answers to the questions. Ask them to explain their reasoning.

> Is this a fair game? Why or why not? *(The game is not fair because each player does not have the same expected score for a given number of turns.)*

Collect some of the individual data from various pairs, and ask students whether the game seems fair based on their individual data. (Although 24 is a small number of turns, most pairs' data will probably be fairly close to the theoretical results of 50% match and 50% no-match. Thus, the chance of getting a match versus a no-match is fair, but the awarding of different numbers of points for these two occurrences makes the game unfair.)

Combine all the data that pairs collected, and determine the experimental probability of a match and a no-match based on the entire set of data by adding the total number of matches and the total number of no-matches. Then, help the class review how to use experimental probabilities to make predictions.

> Based on the experimental probabilities we found for the class data, do you think this game is fair? Why or why not?

Next, discuss the theoretical probabilities.

> What are all the possible outcomes of one turn in this game?

The four possible outcomes are blue/blue, blue/yellow, yellow/blue, and yellow/yellow. Students may think that blue/yellow and yellow/blue are equivalent. Help them understand that although they both give a no-match, they are different outcomes.

> What is the theoretical probability of getting a match? ($\frac{2}{4}$ or $\frac{1}{2}$) What is the theoretical probability of getting a no-match? ($\frac{2}{4}$ or $\frac{1}{2}$)

> How do these theoretical probabilities compare to the experimental probabilities we found from our class data?

If the class's experimental probabilities differ from the theoretical probabilities, talk about the possible reasons for the discrepancy. The experimental probabilities from the class data are probably closer to the theoretical probabilities than those based on the individual pairs' data.

> Considering the theoretical probabilities, do you think this game is fair? Why or why not?

If the game were played 100 times, Player A would expect to win 50 times and score $50 \times 1 = 50$ points. Player B would expect to win 50 times and score $50 \times 2 = 100$ points. Therefore, the game is not fair. As each player has the same chance of scoring (match and no-match are equally likely events), each player should receive the same number of points per win to make the game fair.

Discuss the follow-up questions. Having some pairs share their graphs of their data (from follow-up question 3) and extending that graph with other students' data should help you demonstrate the idea that as more data are collected, the difference between the experimental and theoretical probabilities should decrease.

> How is this game similar to tossing a coin twice? (Tossing a coin twice has four possible outcomes, with a match and no-match equally likely.)

Could you use number cubes to play the Match/No-Match game? How? *(You could roll two number cubes, or roll one number cube twice. If they show the same number, the roll is a match; if they show different numbers, the roll is a no-match.)*

Would Match/No-Match be a fair game if it were played with number cubes? Why?

The game would not be fair, because there are 6 ways to get a match and 30 ways to get a no-match. Students may not know how to find how many ways there are to get a no-match but should realize that there are more ways to get a no-match than a match. To make it a fair game, the scoring system would have to be adjusted.

Would Match/No-Match be a fair game played with number cubes if you used odds and evens? Two even numbers or two odd numbers would count as a match, and an even and an odd number together would count as a no-match.

This game would be fair, because there are four equally likely outcomes: odd/odd, even/even, even/odd, and odd/even.

1.3 • Making Purple

In this problem, students explore a game played with two spinners and continue to analyze two-stage outcomes. An outcome in this game is the combination of the results on the two spinners—for example, green/orange. The follow-up questions lay the groundwork for discussion of expected value.

Launch

Describe the Making Purple game to the class. Demonstrate one or two turns on the two spinners, using a transparency of Labsheet 1.3 if possible.

Ask the class whether they think the game is fair. Most students will intuitively know the game is not fair but will not be sure how to find the probability of making purple. Some may think that the probability of making purple is $\frac{1}{3}$ because the spinners are divided into thirds; others may think that the probability of making purple is $\frac{1}{6}$ because there are two spinners. Again, don't confirm or refute their conjectures; these ideas will be revisited in the summary.

Read the problem with the class so that students have a sense of what is expected of them. Distribute Labsheet 1.3 and two paper clips to each pair, and have them work on the problem. Save the follow-up for after the summary.

Explore

Circulate as pairs work, assisting those who are having trouble analyzing this two-stage game. This problem asks many questions similar to those asked in Problem 1.2. Revisiting these questions gives you a chance to help students who struggled with Problem 1.2.

Summarize

Solicit students' strategies for finding the experimental and theoretical probabilities for making purple. To find the experimental probabilities, students will analyze their data, counting the number of times purple was made and writing a ratio that compares this amount to the total number of trials. To find the theoretical probabilities, many students will have made a list of the possible outcomes; for example:

Spinner A	Spinner B	Purple?
brown	blue	no
brown	orange	no
brown	yellow	no
red	blue	yes
red	orange	no
red	yellow	no
green	blue	no
green	orange	no
green	yellow	no

$P(purple) = \frac{1}{9}$ $P(not\ purple) = \frac{8}{9}$

This list shows all possible outcomes. The set of all possible outcomes in a situation is sometimes called a *sample space*.

By this time, students should accept that the experimental and theoretical probabilities will not necessarily be the same, but that as the sample size increases, the experimental probabilities will get closer to the theoretical probabilities. Again, comparing the combined class data with the data of individual pairs should help you to make this point. If students are struggling with this idea, you could review with the class the graph of one pair's data for part B.

Once you have summarized the problem, arrange students in small groups to talk about the follow-up questions. Give them a few minutes to form some ideas and opinions, and then discuss the questions as a class.

If 36 people play the game, the school would take in $36 \times \$2 = \$72$. The school could expect purple to be made four times, so they could expect to pay out $4 \times \$5 = \$20$, thus making a profit of about $52.

Pose the following questions to check students' understanding.

> Suppose the brown section on spinner A were changed to blue and the yellow section on spinner B were changed to red. How would this change the possible outcomes?

The possible outcomes are now as follows:

Spinner A	Spinner B	Purple?
blue	blue	no
blue	orange	no
blue	red	yes
red	blue	yes
red	orange	no
red	red	no
green	blue	no
green	orange	no
green	red	no

$P(purple) = \frac{2}{9}$ $P(not\ purple) = \frac{7}{9}$

Suppose the brown section on spinner A were changed to red and the yellow section on spinner B were changed to blue. How would this change the possible outcomes?

The possible outcomes are now as follows:

Spinner A	Spinner B	Purple?
red	blue	yes
red	orange	no
red	blue	yes
red	blue	yes
red	orange	no
red	blue	yes
green	blue	no
green	orange	no
green	blue	no

$$P(\text{purple}) = \frac{4}{9} \qquad P(\text{not purple}) = \frac{5}{9}$$

In all of these versions, the game favors the school. However, the school could expect to make the most money with the original version and lose money with the last version.

1.4 • Making Counting Trees

This problem introduces the use of counting trees as a way to analyze some probability situations. In situations in which each outcome is equally likely, counting trees are a useful tool for creating a list of all possible outcomes. (We will not use counting trees to analyze situations in which the outcomes are not equally likely. They can be used in such situations, but the branches must be weighted to reflect the respective probabilities.)

Launch

Use the example in the student edition to illustrate how to make a counting tree. Have students make the counting tree as you draw it at the board or overhead projector. Review how to read the branches from left to right to list all the possible outcomes and how to use the list to determine the theoretical probability of each outcome. Once the list is complete, computing the probabilities is a matter of counting all the entries in the list to determine the denominator and counting the favorable outcomes to find the numerator for the probability of interest.

Read through the problem with the class.

Explore

Let students work individually for a few minutes to make their own counting trees, then gather in groups of two or three to compare results and answer the questions.

Some students will need help getting started. You many want to suggest that they label the stages of the tree (First spin, Second spin) as illustrated in the student edition.

Assign the follow-up to be done after each group has discussed the problem and answered the questions. Each student should make his or her own counting trees for part a of questions 1 and 2, then compare results in their groups.

Summarize

Call on some students to share their counting trees. Ask questions to verify that students can read a counting tree to make a list of the possible outcomes and then use the list to find the probability of a match and the probability of a no-match.

Discuss the follow-up questions to check on students' understanding of how to make and use counting trees.

Additional Answers

Answers to Problem 1.1 Follow-Up

1. a. Each block is equally likely to be selected if the blocks are thoroughly mixed and drawn at random. There is nothing that would give one block a higher probability of being drawn than another.

    b. Each color is not equally likely to be selected. The numbers of the three colors are not equal, so the probabilities of drawing each color are different.

2. The probability of drawing a white block is 0.

3. To make the number of blue blocks (4) equal to the number of yellow and red blocks (8 + 12 = 20), 16 blue blocks must be added.

Answers to Problem 1.2 Follow-Up

1. Yes, the events are equally likely. There are two ways to get a match (yellow/yellow and blue/blue) and two ways to get a no-match (blue/yellow and yellow/blue).

2. a. A spin of two yellows is expected 1 out of 4 turns, a probability of $\frac{1}{4}$. Two yellows can be expected $\frac{1}{4} \times 100 = 25$ times.

    b. A spin of two blues is expected 1 out of 4 times, a probability of $\frac{1}{4}$. Two blues can be expected $\frac{1}{4} \times 100 = 25$ times.

    c. A spin of one yellow and one blue can occur in either order, blue/yellow or yellow/blue, and can be expected 2 out of 4 turns, a probability of $\frac{2}{4}$ or $\frac{1}{2}$. The event can be expected 50 turns out of 100.

    d. At least one yellow occurs with blue/yellow, yellow/blue, or yellow/yellow and can be expected 3 out of 4 turns, or 75 out of 100 turns.

3. a. Possible answer:

Result	P(match)
yellow/yellow	1.00
yellow/blue	0.50
blue/yellow	0.33
blue/yellow	0.25
blue/blue	0.40
yellow/yellow	0.50
blue/blue	0.57
yellow/blue	0.50
blue/blue	0.56
yellow/blue	0.50
yellow/blue	0.45
blue/yellow	0.42

Result	P(match)
blue/blue	0.46
yellow/blue	0.43
blue/blue	0.47
blue/yellow	0.44
blue/blue	0.47
yellow/yellow	0.50
yellow/yellow	0.53
yellow/blue	0.50
yellow/yellow	0.52
yellow/yellow	0.55
blue/blue	0.57
yellow/blue	0.54

b. Possible graph (the points are connected to show the trend in the data):

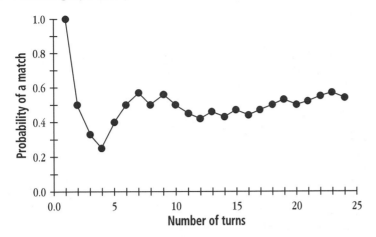

c. The probability of a match would get closer and closer to 0.5 as more data were collected, so the variation from 0.5 would decrease and the line would flatten out. (Note: This is alluding to the Law of Large Numbers: more trials of an experimental situation allow a better approximation of the theoretical probability.)

Answers to Problem 1.3

B. Here are one pair's results:

Turns	Wins	Running probability
5	0	0
10	0	0
15	1	0.07
20	0	0.05
25	1	0.08
30	1	0.10
35	2	0.14
40	0	0.13
45	0	0.11
50	0	0.10

In this example, 5 out of 50 spins, or 10% of the spins, resulted in purple. The graph for these data is as follows (the probability of purple is computed after each set of five trials, and the points are connected to show the trend in the data):

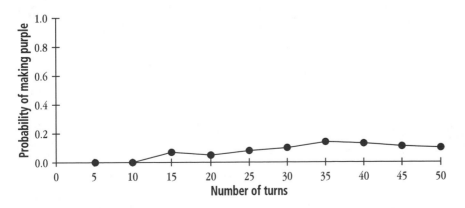

F. As the number of trials increases, the experimental and theoretical probabilities get closer together. With more and more trials, the fluctuations in the experimental probability become less and less noticeable until they are almost undetectable.

Answers to Problem 1.3 Follow-Up

1. You could expect about $\frac{1}{9}$ of the 36 players to win, or about $\frac{1}{9} \times 36 = 4$ players.

2. a. $36 \times \$2 = \$72$

    b. As four of the players could be expected to win, the school could expect to pay out $4 \times \$5 = \$20$.

    c. The school could expect to make $\$72 - \$20 = \$52$.

Answers to Problem 1.4 Follow-Up

1. a.

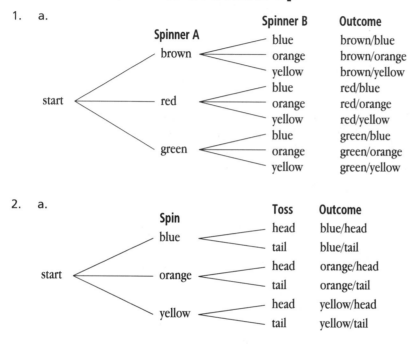

2. a.

ACE Answers

Extensions

20a.

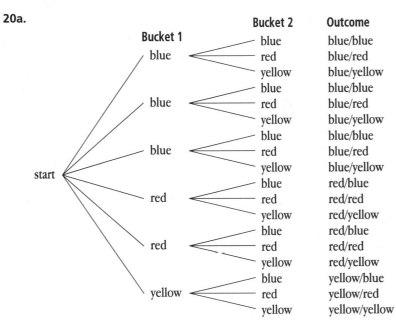

Analyzing Number-Cube Games

This investigation continues the review of some of the basic concepts of probability, including finding experimental probabilities, listing outcomes to find theoretical probabilities, and comparing experimental probabilities with theoretical probabilities. It also continues to lead students toward an understanding of the concept of expected value by asking them to determine whether a game is fair and, if it is not, to find a way to make it fair.

Two games that involve rolling a pair of number cubes and computing with the numbers that are rolled are posed in this investigation. These games involve a greater number of possible outcomes than do the games that students have previously analyzed. In Problem 2.1, Playing the Addition Game, Player A scores 1 point for an odd sum, and Player B scores 1 point for an even sum. The game is fair because the number of odd sums is equal to the number of even sums; the players have an equal chance of scoring a point on each roll. In Problem 2.2, Playing the Multiplication Game, Player A scores 1 point for an odd product, and Player B scores 1 point for an even product. This is not a fair game, as there are more ways to roll even products than odd products.

Mathematical and Problem-Solving Goals

- *To review and develop a deeper understanding of experimental and theoretical probabilities and the relationship between them*

- *To review familiar methods of finding experimental and theoretical probabilities, including experimenting and making an organized list of possible outcomes*

- *To determine whether a game is fair and to find a way to change an unfair game to a fair game by informally applying the concept of expected value*

Materials		
Problem	**For students**	**For the teacher**
All	Graphing calculators, large sheets of paper (optional)	Transparencies 2.1 to 2.2 (optional)
2.1	Labsheet 2.1 (optional; 1 per pair), number cubes (2 per pair)	
2.2	Labsheet 2.2 (optional; 1 per pair), number cubes (2 per pair)	

▼ Student Pages 22–31   Teaching the Investigation 31a–31h

Playing the Addition Game

At a Glance

Grouping:
Pairs

Launch

■ Introduce the Addition Game, and demonstrate a few rolls of a pair of number cubes.

■ Ask the class how they might keep track of their results, and ask for conjectures on whether the game is fair.

Explore

■ Have pairs play the game and answer the questions.

■ Help pairs who are having trouble finding a systematic way of recording their results.

Summarize

■ Ask the class whether the Addition Game is a fair game.

■ Have students share how they kept track of their results.

■ As a class, review all the possible outcomes of a roll of two number cubes and discuss the follow-up.

Assignment Choices

ACE questions 1–6, 11–15, 18, 20–23, and unassigned choices from earlier problems

---

Analyzing Number-Cube Games

In Investigation 1, you used various strategies to find probabilities associated with games of chance. You found *experimental probabilities* by playing a game several times and evaluating the results, and you found *theoretical probabilities* by analyzing the possible outcomes of a game. In this investigation, you will explore experimental and theoretical probabilities involved in some number-cube games.

2.1 Playing the Addition Game

In this problem, you will play the Addition Game with a partner and try to determine whether it is fair.

Addition Game Rules

• Player A and Player B take turns rolling two number cubes.

• If the sum of the numbers rolled is odd, Player A scores 1 point.

• If the sum of the numbers rolled is even, Player B scores 1 point.

• The player with the most points after 36 rolls wins.

> **Problem 2.1**
>
> Play the Addition Game with a partner. Keep track of your results.
>
> **A.** Based on your data, what is the experimental probability of rolling an odd sum? An even sum?
>
> **B.** List all the possible pairs of numbers you can roll with two number cubes.
>
> **C.** What is the theoretical probability of rolling an odd sum? An even sum?
>
> **D.** Do you think the Addition Game is a fair game? Explain why or why not.

Answers to Problem 2.1

A. Answers will vary. See the Summarize section for one pair's results.

B. All the possible pairs of numbers can be found by making an organized list, a counting tree, or a chart; see the examples in the Summarize section.

C. Both theoretical probabilities are $\frac{18}{36}$, or 50%.

D. The Addition Game is a fair game because each player has the same chances of scoring and receives the same number of points for a score.

Problem 2.1 Follow-Up

1. Min-wei invented a game based on the sum of two number cubes. In her game, Player A scores 1 point for sums of 6 or 7, and Player B scores 1 point for any other sum. Min-wei thought this would be a fair game because sums of 6 and 7 occur so often. Is this a fair game? Explain why or why not.

2. Royce invented a game based on the sum of two number cubes. In his game, Player A scores 3 points if the sum is a multiple of 3, and Player B scores 1 point if the sum is *not* a multiple of 3. Is Royce's game a fair game? Explain why or why not.

2.2 Playing the Multiplication Game

In the Addition Game, players score points based on the sum of the numbers rolled on two number cubes. In the Multiplication Game, scoring depends on the *product* of the numbers rolled.

Multiplication Game Rules

- Player A and Player B take turns rolling two number cubes.
- If the product of the numbers rolled is odd, Player A scores 1 point.
- If the product of the numbers rolled is even, Player B scores 1 point.
- The player with the most points after 36 rolls wins.

Problem 2.2

Play the Multiplication Game with a partner. Keep track of your results.

A. Based on your data, what is the experimental probability of rolling an odd product? An even product?

B. What is the theoretical probability of rolling an odd product? An even product?

C. Do you think the Multiplication Game is fair? Explain why or why not.

D. If the game consisted of 100 rolls instead of 36, how many points would you expect each player to have at the end of the game?

Problem 2.2 Follow-Up

1. How could you make the Multiplication Game a fair game?
2. Invent a fair two-person game based on the product of two number cubes. A player should score 1 point each time he or she scores. You will need to decide which player scores on which kinds of products. Explain why your game is fair.

Investigation 2: Analyzing Number-Cube Games **23**

At a Glance

Grouping:
Pairs

Launch

- Introduce the Multiplication Game, and demonstrate a few rolls of two number cubes.

- Ask the class how they might keep track of their results, and ask for conjectures on whether the game is fair and how close the theoretical and experimental probabilities will be.

Explore

- Have pairs play the game and answer the questions.

- Look for students with interesting ways of forming the theoretical probabilities.

- Have pairs do the follow-up.

Summarize

- Review the answers to the questions.

- Help the class pool the data and compare the theoretical and experimental probabilities, then discuss the follow-up.

Answers to Problem 2.1 Follow-Up

1. Min-wei's game is not a fair game of chance. The probability of a score by Player A is $\frac{11}{36}$, the probability of a score by Player B is $\frac{25}{36}$, and the players both receive 1 point each time they score.

2. Royce's game is not a fair game of chance. The probability of a score by Player A is $\frac{12}{36}$, and the probability of a score by Player B is $\frac{24}{36}$. This means that of 36 rolls, Player A could expect 12 scoring opportunities, and Player B could expect 24 scoring opportunities—thus Player A would score 36 points and Player B would score only 24 points.

Answers to Problem 2.2

See page 31g.

Answers to Problem 2.2 Follow-Up

See page 31g.

Assignment Choices

ACE questions 7–10, 16, 17, 19, 24, and unassigned choices from earlier problems

Assessment

It is appropriate to use Check-Up 1 after this problem.

Answers

Applications

1. $\frac{3}{36}$ or $\frac{1}{12}$
2. $\frac{10}{36}$ or $\frac{5}{18}$
3. $\frac{8}{36}$ or $\frac{2}{9}$
4. $\frac{1}{36}$

5a. Students could represent the outcomes in a list or a counting tree.

Spinner	Number cube
1	1
1	2
1	3
1	4
1	5
1	6
2	1
2	2
2	3
2	4
2	5
2	6
3	1
3	2
3	3
3	4
3	5
3	6

5b. $\frac{1}{18}$

5c. $\frac{17}{18}$

5d. $\frac{8}{18}$

Applications • Connections • Extensions

As you work on these ACE questions, use your calculator whenever you need it.

Applications

In 1–4, find the probability of getting the given result when two number cubes are rolled.

1. a sum of 4

2. a sum less than 6

3. a sum of 7 or 11

4. a pair of 5s

5. Suppose you were to spin the spinner below and then roll a number cube.

a. Make an organized list of the possible outcomes.

b. What is the probability that you will get a 1 on both the number cube and the spinner?

c. What is the probability that you will *not* get a 1 on both the number cube and the spinner?

d. What is the probability that you will get a 1 on the number cube or the spinner?

e. What is the probability that you will get the same number on the number cube and the spinner?

f. What is the probability that the sum of the number on the spinner and the number on the number cube will be greater than 8?

g. What is the probability that the product of the number on the spinner and the number on the number cube will be 0?

6. Chris did an experiment using the spinner and number cube from question 5. For each trial, he spun the spinner and then rolled the number cube. He was surprised to find that he got a 1 on both the spinner and the number cube in 4 out of 36 trials.

a. Based on his results, what is the experimental probability of getting a 1 on both the number cube and the spinner?

b. Chris compared the experimental probability of getting a 1 on both the number cube and the spinner to the theoretical probability. He decided that something must be wrong with the spinner or the number cube, since these probabilities are not the same. Do you agree? Why or why not?

7. Raymundo invented the Prime Number Multiplication game. In this game, two number cubes are rolled. Player A scores 10 points if the product is prime, and Player B scores 1 point if the product is not prime. Raymundo thinks this scoring system is reasonable because there are many more ways to roll a nonprime product than a prime product.

a. If the cubes are rolled 100 times, how many points would you expect Player A to score? How many points would you expect Player B to score?

b. Is Raymundo's game a fair game? Explain why or why not.

5e. $\frac{3}{18}$

5f. $\frac{1}{18}$

5g. 0

6a. $\frac{4}{36}$ or $\frac{1}{9}$

6b. no; An experimental probability will not always equal the theoretical probability. Given that there are 18 possible outcomes, 36 is not very many trials from which to determine a probability.

7a. The prime products—2, 3, and 5—can be obtained 6 different ways. The probability of getting a prime product is thus $\frac{6}{36}$ or $\frac{1}{6}$. Out of 100 rolls, Player A can expect a prime number about $\frac{1}{6}$ of the time, or about 17 times, earning about 170 points. Player B can expect a nonprime product about $\frac{5}{6}$ of the time, or about 83 times, earning about 83 points.

7b. Raymundo's game is not fair. Player A can expect to score about twice as many points as Player B. (To make the game fair, Player A could score 5 points for every prime product.)

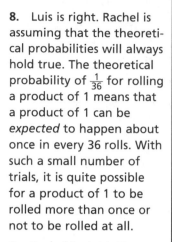

8. Luis is right. Rachel is assuming that the theoretical probabilities will always hold true. The theoretical probability of $\frac{1}{36}$ for rolling a product of 1 means that a product of 1 can be *expected* to happen about once in every 36 rolls. With such a small number of trials, it is quite possible for a product of 1 to be rolled more than once or not to be rolled at all.

9. Rachel is right. The number 23 is prime and could only be obtained by rolling a 1 and a 23, which is impossible.

10a. $\frac{2}{40}$ or $\frac{1}{20}$

10b. She could expect to win about once, since the experimental probability of winning is $\frac{1}{20}$.

10c. It would take 20 tickets for Juanita to play 20 times, and her one expected win would earn her 10 tickets, so she can expect to be behind 10 tickets.

10d. The various outcomes are not equally likely and the situation is very complex, so it is probably impossible to find the theoretical probability of winning. It also probably varies with the skill of the thrower.

8. Rachel says that if she rolls two number cubes 36 times, she will get a product of 1 exactly once. Luis said that she cannot be sure this will happen exactly once, but it will probably happen very few times. Who is right? Explain your reasoning.

9. Rachel told Luis that if she rolls two number cubes 100 times, she will *never* get a product of 23. Luis told her that she can't be sure. Who is right? Explain your reasoning.

10. Juanita is trying to decide whether to play a certain game at an amusement park. It takes one ticket to play the game. A player flips two plastic bottles. If both bottles land standing up, the player wins ten tickets to use for rides and games. Juanita has been watching people play the game for a while and has recorded the results in a table:

Both land on side	One lands on side and one lands standing up	Both land standing up
⊬⊬⊬ ⊬⊬⊬ ⊬⊬⊬ ⊬⊬⊬ ||||	⊬⊬⊬ ⊬⊬⊬ ||||	||

a. Based on Juanita's results, what is the experimental probability of winning the game?

b. If Juanita played this game 20 times, how many times could she expect to win?

c. How many tickets could Juanita expect to be ahead or behind after playing the game 20 times? Explain your reasoning.

d. Is it possible to find the theoretical probability of winning this game? Why or why not?

In 11–15, tell whether theoretical or experimental probability is being used.

11. Kelly played darts on a board made of concentric blue, red, and yellow regions. The dart landed in the red region 7 times and in the other regions a total of 13 times. Kelly stated that on her next throw, the dart has a 35% chance of landing in the red region.

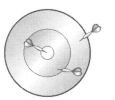

12. For 10 minutes before school each day, some students from Ms. MacAfee's class recorded the types of vehicles that passed by the school. They wanted to figure out whether it was more likely for a car or a truck to pass by. After a week of observing, the students used their data to predict that a car is more likely to pass by than a truck.

13. Emma is in the fun house at the amusement park. She must choose from among three exits. At one exit, visitors get squirted with water. At another exit, visitors get sprayed with whipped cream. At a third exit, visitors must walk through mud. Emma does not know which exit is which. She decides that if she selects an exit at random, she has a $\frac{1}{3}$ chance of getting sprayed with whipped cream.

14. Waldo buys a pair of weighted number cubes at a novelty store. In 30 rolls, he gets a sum of 2 eleven times. Waldo figures that if he rolls the number cubes 100 times, he will get a sum of 2 about 37 times.

15. Tina keeps a pack of 20 colored pencils in her backpack. When her science teacher asks the students to design a cover for their science projects, Tina pulls out a colored pencil without looking. She figures she has about a 5% chance of picking her favorite color, orange.

11. experimental probability

12. experimental probability

13. theoretical probability

14. experimental probability

15. theoretical probability

Investigation 2: Analyzing Number-Cube Games 27

Connections

16a. See below right.

16b. blue/1, blue/2, blue/3, blue/3, red/1, red/2, red/3, red/3, red/1, red/2, red/3, red/3, green/1, green/2, green/3, green/3, yellow/1, yellow/2, yellow/3, yellow/3

16c. red/3 (It can occur four different ways.)

16d. $\frac{4}{20}$ or $\frac{1}{5}$

16e. $\frac{10}{20}$ or $\frac{1}{2}$

17a. $\frac{11}{36}$

17b. $\frac{11}{36} \times 100 =$ about 31 times

17c. 0

17d. 0; You can never roll a multiple of 7.

Connections

16. Marinda and Isaiah are analyzing a game involving two different spinners. For each turn, a player spins each spinner once. To help them find theoretical probabilities, Marinda and Isaiah made the counting tree at right.

   a. Design two spinners that could be the spinners used by Marinda and Isaiah.

   b. List all the possible outcomes of spinning each spinner once.

   c. Which color/number combination has the greatest probability of occurring?

   d. Based on your spinners, what is the probability of getting red on spinner A and 3 on spinner B?

   e. Based on your spinners, what is the probability of *not* getting 3 on spinner B?

17. **a.** When you roll two number cubes, what is the probability that the product of the numbers will be a multiple of 5?

   b. If you roll two number cubes 100 times, about how many times can you expect the product to be a multiple of 5?

   c. What is the probability of rolling a product that is a multiple of 7?

   d. If you roll two number cubes a million times, how many times can you expect to get a product that is a multiple of 7?

16a. Possible answer:

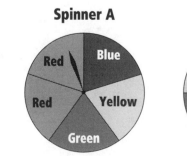

Spinner A   Spinner B

18. David went to Miceli's Deli for lunch. He saw the sign below:

Sandwich Special:
choose 1 bread, 1 meat, and 1 cheese — $1.79

 ▢ Breads	🫓 Meats	△ Cheeses
Rye	Turkey	Swiss
White	Ham	Cheddar
	Salami	Mozzarella

David couldn't decide which kind of sandwich he wanted, so he told the sandwich maker to surprise him. If the sandwich maker chooses the bread, meat, and cheese at random, what is the probability that David will get a turkey sandwich on white bread with cheddar cheese? Explain your reasoning.

19. Tricia wants to determine the probability of getting two 1s when two number cubes are rolled. She made a counting tree and used it to list the possible outcomes.

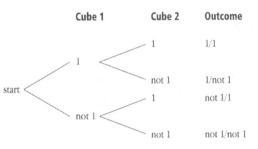

Cube 1	Cube 2	Outcome

She says that, since there are four possible outcomes, the probability of getting 1 on both number cubes is $\frac{1}{4}$. Is Tricia right? Why or why not?

18. See page 31h.

19. The way Tricia has constructed her counting tree, the four outcomes are *not* equally likely. This leads to her incorrect reasoning that the probability of getting a 1 on both number cubes is $\frac{1}{4}$. In fact, there are 36 possible equally likely outcomes for a roll of two number cubes, and only one is (1, 1), so the probability is actually $\frac{1}{36}$.

20a. $\frac{12}{44}$ or about 27%

20b. $\frac{10}{42}$ or about 24%

Extensions

21. Two possible games are described here. *Game 1:* Three coins are tossed. If all three land heads up, Player A scores 1 point. If all three land tails up, Player B scores 1 point. This game is fair because TTT and HHH both have a probability of $\frac{1}{8}$. *Game 2:* Three coins are tossed. If all three match, Player A scores 6 points. If they don't all match, Player B scores 2 points. This game is fair because TTT and HHH together have a probability of $\frac{2}{8}$ and the remaining outcomes have a probability of $\frac{6}{8}$.

22. Each of the 36 possible outcomes for two number cubes could be combined with the 6 outcomes for the third number cube, for 36 × 6 = 216 possible equally likely outcomes. Six of these—111, 222, 333, 444, 555, and 666—are triple matches, with a probability of $\frac{6}{216}$ or $\frac{1}{36}$.

23. The only way to get a product greater than 200 is to roll three 6s, with a probability of $\frac{1}{216}$.

24. See right.

20. The authors of this book surveyed middle school students from several schools across the country to try to determine what interests middle school students. One question they asked was: "How interested are you in bicycling?" The bar graphs below show the results for 44 girls and 42 boys.

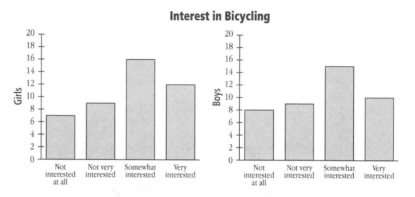

Interest in Bicycling

a. Based on the results of the survey, what is the probability that a middle school girl will say she is very interested in bicycling?

b. Based on the results of the survey, what is the probability that a middle school boy will say he is very interested in bicycling?

Extensions

21. Make up a fair game that involves tossing three coins. Describe the rules of your game, and explain why your game is fair.

22. When you roll three number cubes, what is the probability that all three numbers will match?

23. When you roll three number cubes, what is the probability that the product of the numbers will be greater than 200?

24. Matthew invented a two-person game in which players take turns rolling three number cubes. If the sum is even, Player A scores 1 point. If the sum is odd, Player B scores 1 point. Is Matthew's game a fair game? Explain why or why not.

30 What Do You Expect?

24. Making a counting tree for this situation would be quite cumbersome, given the 216 outcomes. Instead, students might use what they learned in Problem 2.1. With two number cubes, the probabilities for rolling an odd or an even sum are equal. The third number cube could come up either odd or even. If it is even, the previous even sums stay even and the odd sums stay odd. If it is odd, the previous even sums become odd and the odd sums become even. The split between odd and even sums stays the same, making Matthew's game fair.

Mathematical Reflections

In this investigation, you looked at games involving number cubes. You determined whether games were fair and figured out how you could change the rules of an unfair game to make it a fair game. These questions will help you summarize what you have learned:

1 What does it mean for a game of chance to be fair?

2 Create a game that is not fair. How can you adjust the system of scoring to make the game fair?

3 In a game of chance, how can you predict the number of times out of 100 a certain outcome will occur? Give an example if it helps you to explain your thinking.

Think about your answers to these questions, discuss your ideas with other students and your teacher, and then write a summary of your findings in your journal.

Tips for the Linguistically Diverse Classroom

Original Rebus The Original Rebus technique is described in detail in *Getting to Know Connected Mathematics*. Students make a copy of the text before it is discussed. During the discussion, they generate their own rebuses for words they do not understand; the words are made comprehensible through pictures, objects, or demonstrations. Example: Question 1—Key phrases for which students might make rebuses are *game of chance* (a question mark), *fair* (balancing scale).

Possible Answers

1. A game of chance is fair if the players have the same probability of scoring a given number of points. In the long run, every player should expect to win the same number of points.

2. To make an unfair game fair, you need to change the scoring system so that the players can expect to earn the same number of points. Suppose in a two-person game that Player A is three times as likely to score as is Player B. Player B needs to be awarded three times the number of points for a score as Player A earns for a score.

3. To predict the number of times an outcome will occur, you can find either a theoretical probability (if that is possible) or an experimental probability. To find the number of times an outcome will occur using a theoretical probability, you first need to determine the probability that the outcome will occur. To do this, you can make a table, a counting tree, or an organized list of possible outcomes. Then, you multiply the probability by 100. To find an experimental probability, you need to gather enough data to be able to make a good guess. The more data you gather, the closer your experimental probability will be to the theoretical probability. Then, you multiply this probability by 100.

TEACHING THE INVESTIGATION

2.1 • Playing the Addition Game

In Investigation 1, students made lists of possible outcomes to determine theoretical probabilities. To find the theoretical probabilities of the outcomes in the Addition Game in Problem 2.1 and the Product Game in Problem 2.2, students must find a way to make an organized list of a larger sample space than they have previously encountered. There are 36 possible pairs of numbers that can be rolled with two number cubes.

Launch

Introduce the Addition Game, and demonstrate a couple of rolls of two number cubes. If possible, use two different colors of number cubes to help students to see, for example, that 2 and 3 is not the same as 3 and 2. After each roll, ask the class who scores on that roll. If the sum of the two numbers shown is odd, Player A scores 1 point. If the sum is even, Player B scores 1 point.

> How could you and your partner keep track of your results?

Some students may suggest keeping a list of the sums. Others might suggest keeping track of the outcomes of each number cube as well as the sums.

> What are the possible outcomes of adding the numbers shown on a roll of two number cubes? *(2, 3, 4, 5, 6, 7, 8, 9, 10, 11, and 12)*

> Based on this information, the rolls we have taken, and your experience with rolling number cubes, do you think the Addition Game is fair?

Let students offer their conjectures. If some claim that the game is unfair, ask whom the game favors and why they think so. Don't confirm any of their conjectures at this time; you will return to this idea in the summary of the problem. Some students think the game favors the evens because there are six even sums but only five odd sums. Again, this can be explored mathematically in the summary.

Take a few minutes to talk about how to conduct this experiment.

> We want the results of the number-cube rolls to be *random*—that is, we do not want anything about the way we roll the number cubes to bias the results. What sorts of things might bias our results? *(always holding the cubes a certain way, using cubes that are flawed, and so on)*

Distribute two number cubes to each pair of students. Hand out Labsheet 2.1 for pairs to record their data, or let them find their own methods of keeping track of their results.

Explore

As you watch students play, ask them whether they think the game is fair. Look for interesting ways they have of reasoning about the game and recording their experimental results.

If students are having trouble finding a way to systematically list the outcomes in part B so they can find the theoretical probabilities of rolling even and odd sums, you might suggest that they use a counting tree.

Summarize

Once students have finished answering the questions, bring the class back together. Ask students to share how they kept track of their results.

A line plot is one useful method for collecting such data. You may want to demonstrate this by making a line plot on the board of one pair's data; for example:

```
                    X
                X   X
                X   X
                X   X   X
            X   X   X   X   X   X   X
        X   X   X   X   X   X   X   X   X   X
    X   X   X   X   X   X   X   X   X   X   X
    ─────────────────────────────────────────
    2   3   4   5   6   7   8   9   10  11  12
```

From the line plot, we can quickly see that rolling a sum of 6, 7, or 8 is more likely than rolling a sum of 2, 3, 11, or 12. Based on the data shown in this line plot, the probability of rolling an even sum is $\frac{19}{36}$, and the probability of rolling an odd sum is $\frac{17}{36}$. If one were to continue to add data to the line plot, not only would the probability of rolling an odd or an even sum get very close to $\frac{1}{2}$, but the data would yield probabilities for specific sums that were very close to their theoretical probabilities.

> When you played the game, did you get an equal number of odd and even sums?
>
> Do you think the Addition Game is a fair game? Why or why not?

Most, or all, of the students will say that the Addition Game is a fair game of chance.

Discuss with the class how you might pool, in a uniform way, all the data that the class has generated. Then, collect all the data.

> For our combined data, what is the experimental probability of rolling an even sum? Of rolling an odd sum?
>
> How did you find these probabilities?
>
> Do you think we have enough rolls of the number cubes to feel confident about the accuracy of the experimental probabilities we have found?

Part B of the problem asks students to list all the possible pairs of numbers that can be rolled with two number cubes. To find the theoretical probabilities in part C, students will have to have found a way to list all the possible sums. There are several ways students might have approached this. For example, students might have made counting trees.

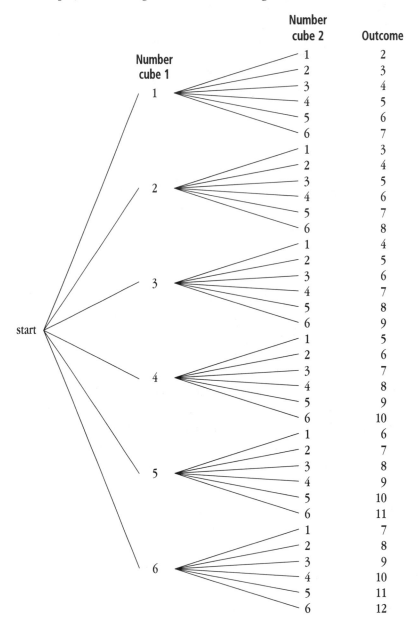

Some students might have used an organizing scheme such as the following:

(1, 1) → 2	(2, 1) → 3	(3, 1) → 4	(4, 1) → 5	(5, 1) → 6	(6, 1) → 7
(1, 2) → 3	(2, 2) → 4	(3, 2) → 5	(4, 2) → 6	(5, 2) → 7	(6, 2) → 8
(1, 3) → 4	(2, 3) → 5	(3, 3) → 6	(4, 3) → 7	(5, 3) → 8	(6, 3) → 9
(1, 4) → 5	(2, 4) → 6	(3, 4) → 7	(4, 4) → 8	(5, 4) → 9	(6, 4) → 10
(1, 5) → 6	(2, 5) → 7	(3, 5) → 8	(4, 5) → 9	(5, 5) → 10	(6, 5) → 11
(1, 6) → 7	(2, 6) → 8	(3, 6) → 9	(4, 6) → 10	(5, 6) → 11	(6, 6) → 12

Students who have completed the grade 6 probability unit *How Likely Is It?* might have used a chart like the one below. Each cell in the chart represents the sum of the numbers rolled. For example, in the first row, the roll (1, 1) gives a sum of 2, the roll (1, 2) gives a sum of 3, and the roll (1, 3) gives a sum of 4.

Number cube 1

+	1	2	3	4	5	6
1	2	3	4	5	6	7
2	3	4	5	6	7	8
3	4	5	6	7	8	9
4	5	6	7	8	9	10
5	6	7	8	9	10	11
6	7	8	9	10	11	12

Number cube 2

If none of your students suggests such a chart as a means of finding all the possible sums, present the idea yourself. Finding the theoretical probabilities from this chart is easy.

Next, help the class use this chart to compare the theoretical probabilities to the class's experimental probabilities. Ask questions to help students understand this analysis.

How many ways are there to get an even sum? *(18)*

How many ways are there to get an odd sum? *(18)*

Does each player have an equal chance of winning this game? Why or why not? *(Yes; each player has an $\frac{18}{36}$, or 50%, chance of winning the game.)*

With this chart displayed, you can ask other questions to help students review concepts about factors and multiples.

What is the probability of getting a sum that is
- a prime number? *($\frac{15}{36}$ or $\frac{5}{12}$)*
- a multiple of 5? *($\frac{7}{36}$)*
- a multiple of 2 and 3? *($\frac{6}{36}$ or $\frac{1}{6}$)*
- a factor of 24? *($\frac{17}{36}$)*
- a multiple of 15? *(0)*

If you roll the number cubes 100 times, how many times could you expect to get a sum that is a factor of 15? *(about 17 times)*

How did you find this amount? *(Of the possible sums, $\frac{6}{36}$, or $\frac{1}{6}$, are factors of 15, and $\frac{1}{6}$ of 100 is $16\frac{2}{3}$, or about 17.)*

This analysis leads naturally into a discussion of the follow-up questions. When students have agreed that the game in follow-up question 2 is unfair, ask for new scoring rules that would change it to a fair game. For example, if the rules gave Player A 2 points each time a multiple of 3 was rolled, the game could be fair because each player could expect 24 points.

2.2 • Playing the Multiplication Game

In this game, points are assigned to players based on whether the product, rather than the sum, of the two numbers rolled on a pair of number cubes is odd or even.

Launch

Introduce the Multiplication Game, and demonstrate a few rolls. After each roll, ask the class who scores on that roll. If the product of the two numbers shown is odd, Player A scores 1 point. If the product is even, Player B scores 1 point.

Ask students whether they think the game is fair, and let them offer their conjectures. Most will probably say it is, since the Addition Game is fair. You will return to this question in the summary of the problem.

Discuss the possible events for a roll.

> What products are possible when you roll two number cubes? *(1, 2, 3, 4, 5, 6, 8, 9, 10, 12, 15, 16, 18, 20, 24, 25, 30, and 36)*

Remind pairs that when they play the Multiplication Game, they will need to keep track of how many times each of these possibilities is rolled and whether the product is even or odd.

> When you have finished your experiment, you will need to find a way to analyze the game theoretically.

> When you compare your experimental probabilities to the theoretical probabilities, do you think they will be close? Exactly the same? Why or why not?

> If we pool all our data, will the new experimental probabilities we get be closer to the theoretical probabilities? Why or why not?

Distribute two number cubes to each pair. Hand out Labsheet 2.2 for students to record their data, or let them find their own method of keeping track of their results.

Explore

By this time, most students should feel comfortable with experimenting to find experimental probabilities and analyzing a game to find theoretical probabilities. Be on the lookout for students with interesting ways of thinking about how to compute the theoretical probabilities for this game.

Students often recognize that when one number cube is rolled, the chances of getting an odd or an even number are equal. Some may further reason that because odd × odd = odd, even × even = even, odd × even = even, and even × odd = even, and as these are all equally likely, there are three out of four ways to get an even product. However, some students who reason this way miss reversing the even-odd combination and state the theoretical probability of getting an even product as $\frac{2}{3}$ rather than $\frac{3}{4}$. If this occurs, you will want to be sure to discuss this idea in the summary and have someone explain why $\frac{2}{3}$ is not the probability.

When pairs finish working on the problem, have them move on to the follow-up.

Summarize

Begin by reviewing part C of the problem, which asks whether the game is fair, then address parts A and B. Students could simply discuss their solutions to these questions, or each pair could record their answers on large sheets of paper to be displayed and discussed.

To look more closely at the results of students' experimentation, you may want to make a line plot that shows the number of times each product came up as your students played the game. Below is the beginning of a class line plot, with one pair's data displayed.

Once the data from the entire class have been pooled, the class can compute the overall experimental probabilities and use them to predict which products occur most often and whether or not the game is fair. It would be helpful for each pair of students to compare the experimental probabilities from their own data with the experimental probabilities from the class data. The accumulated data should make it clear that odd products occur only about 25% of the time.

Part B asks students to find the theoretical probability of rolling an even or an odd product. Students may have made an organized list, a counting tree, or a chart to show all the possibilities. If no one suggests using a chart like the one shown below, present the idea yourself.

Number cube 1

×	1	2	3	4	5	6
1	1	2	3	4	5	6
2	2	4	6	8	10	12
3	3	6	9	12	15	18
4	4	8	12	16	20	24
5	5	10	15	20	25	30
6	6	12	18	24	30	36

(Number cube 2 labels the rows)

Ask how the experimental probabilities based on the class data compare to the theoretical probabilities. If they do not match—and they may not—ask whether that means that there is something wrong with the collected data or with the theoretical probabilities. Students need to think and talk about the relationship between experimental probabilities and theoretical probabilities, continuing to question what the two mean and how each can be used to make sense of probability situations.

With this chart displayed, you can ask questions about the probability of getting primes, factors, and multiples.

What is the probability of getting a product that is
- a multiple of 3? ($\frac{20}{36}$ or $\frac{5}{9}$)
- a multiple of 2 or 3? ($\frac{3}{36}$ or $\frac{1}{12}$)
- a factor of both 12 and 15? ($\frac{3}{36}$ or $\frac{1}{12}$)
- greater than 12? ($\frac{13}{36}$)

Discuss the follow-up questions. Ask students to share their ideas of how to assign points to make the Multiplication Game fair. Have some explain their scoring rules for a new two-person game, while the class makes sure the proposed rules give each player the same chances to score.

Additional Answers

Answers to Problem 2.2

A. Answers will vary.

B. P(odd product) = $\frac{9}{36}$, P(even product) = $\frac{27}{36}$

C. The game is not fair. Player B, who scores on even products, has a much greater chance of winning.

D. In 100 trials, Player A could be expected to score 25 times (for 25 points) while Player B could be expected to score 75 times (for 75 points).

Answers to Problem 2.2 Follow-Up

1. Possible answer: If Player A scores 3 points for an odd product, Player A could be expected to score 25 × 3 = 75 points on 100 rolls. This matches Player B's expected 75 points from 75 rolls.

2. Possible answer: If the product of the numbers rolled is prime, Player A scores 1 point. If the product is a multiple of 10, Player B scores 1 point. This gives each player six possibilities—2, 2, 3, 3, 5, 5 versus 10, 10, 20, 20, 30, 30—on which to score.

ACE Answers

Connections

18. As the counting tree shows, there are 18 possible outcomes, one of which is turkey with cheddar on white bread. The probability is $\frac{1}{18}$.

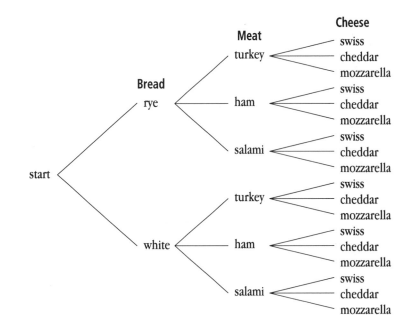

Probability and Area

This investigation introduces students to relating probabilities to the area of a grid, which helps prepare them for analyzing probabilities using the area model introduced in Investigation 4. In working through this investigation, students continue to think about other probability concepts, such as equally likely versus non–equally likely outcomes. Connections to geometry are embedded throughout the investigation and the ACE questions.

The context of this investigation is a computer game in which the floor plan of an imaginary castle is set on a grid. In Problem 3.1, Cracking Level 1, students find the theoretical probability that a treasure is hidden in one of the rooms on the first floor of a palace, which is set up on a 10 by 10 grid. The probability that the treasure is in a given room is equal to the part out of 100 that is represented by the area of the room. In Problem 3.2, Cracking Level 2, students move on to the second floor of the palace. They find the theoretical probability that the treasure is hidden in one of the rooms or in a collection of rooms, which requires finding the part of the total floor plan occupied by each room.

Mathematical and Problem-Solving Goals

- *To review and come to a deeper understanding of experimental and theoretical probabilities and the relationship between them*

- *To begin thinking about probabilities in terms of areas on a grid as an introduction to the area model for analyzing probabilities*

Materials		
Problem	For students	For the teacher
All	Graphing calculators	Transparencies 3.1A to 3.2C (optional)
3.1	Computers and the Treasure Hunt program (optional; see the Technology section in the introduction)	
3.2	Grid paper (for students who want it)	

Student Pages 32–40   Teaching the Investigation 40a–40c

3.1

Cracking Level 1

At a Glance

Grouping:
Small Groups

Launch

- Talk about the Treasure Hunt computer game and how it hides the treasure.

- If you have a computer and the Treasure Hunt program, demonstrate the game.

- Ask students which room they would guess first.

Explore

- Have groups first play the game on a computer if possible.

- When they have finished the problem, have groups answer the follow-up questions.

Summarize

- Discuss the problem and follow-up.

- Ask questions to highlight the connection between the area of a room and the probability of the treasure being hidden there.

Assignment Choices

ACE questions 1, 5–8, and unassigned choices from earlier problems (students may want grid paper for 8)

INVESTIGATION 3

Probability and Area

In this investigation, you will explore a computer game called Treasure Hunt, which involves searching for treasure in a royal palace. You will see how you can use theoretical probability to improve your chances of winning the game.

3.1 Cracking Level 1

When you play the first level of the Treasure Hunt game, the computer hides a treasure on the first floor of the palace. The floor plan is pictured here.

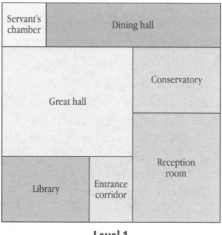

Level 1

The computer gives the player clues about where the treasure is located. After each clue, the player must guess which room the treasure is in. The computer continues to give clues until the player finds the treasure. The fewer clues the player needs to find the treasure, the more points the player gets.

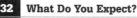

32 What Do You Expect?

Tips for the Linguistically Diverse Classroom

Visual Enhancement The Visual Enhancement technique is described in detail in *Getting to Know Connected Mathematics*. It involves using real objects or pictures to make information more comprehensible. Example: When discussing the floor plan for the Treasure Hunt game, you might show pictures of the rooms being identified.

To make good guesses when playing Treasure Hunt, it helps to understand how the computer hides the treasure. The computer "thinks" of the first floor of the palace as a 10 by 10 grid. At the start of a game, the computer **randomly** selects one of the 100 squares as the location for the treasure. For example, if the computer selects the square indicated on the left grid below, the treasure is hidden in the conservatory.

Think about this!

Suppose the computer gives you this first clue:

The treasure is hidden in a room with "hall" in its name.

Which room should you guess first? Explain your answer.

Cracking Level 2

Grouping:
Small Groups

Launch

- Talk about level 2 of the Treasure Hunt game.

- Make sure students see the connection between probability and area, which they discovered in Problem 3.1, and the level 2 layout, which is not on a grid.

Explore

- Have groups work on the problem and follow-up.

- Work with any students who are having trouble understanding the relationship between probability and area.

Summarize

- Let students share their answers to the problem.

- Discuss working with rounded numbers.

- Talk about the probabilities of 0 and 1, as brought out in the follow-up.

Problem 3.1

A. How can this information about how the computer hides the treasure help you find the treasure?

B. You have just entered level 1 of Treasure Hunt. What is the probability that the treasure is hidden in the great hall? In the servant's chamber?

C. If you play level 1 ten times, how many times can you expect the treasure to be hidden in the great hall? In the servant's chamber?

Problem 3.1 Follow-Up

1. The first time you play level 1, the treasure is hidden in the library. What is the probability that the treasure will be hidden in the library the second time you play level 1?

2. Monty says that since the computer randomly picks the location of the treasure, the treasure is just as likely to be hidden in the entrance corridor as in the great hall. Is Monty correct? Explain your answer.

3.2 Cracking Level 2

For the second level of the Treasure Hunt game, a player must find a hidden treasure on the second floor of the palace. The second floor has rooms for the king's and queen's servants. As in level 1, the computer "thinks" of the floor as a grid and hides the treasure by randomly selecting a grid square. However, notice that the floor of level 2 is *not* a square.

Queen's lady-in-waiting's room	King's steward's room
	King's chancellor's room
Queen's maid's room	King's marshal's room

Level 2

Assignment Choices

ACE questions 2–4, 9, and unassigned choices from earlier problems

Assessment

It is appropriate to use Quiz A after this problem.

Answers to Problem 3.1

A. The computer randomly assigns the treasure to one of the 100 squares in the grid. Therefore, the probability that the treasure is hidden in a particular room depends on the area of the room.

B. P(great hall): $\frac{30}{100}$ or 0.30, P(servant's chamber): $\frac{4}{100}$ or 0.04

C. The treasure can be expected to be hidden in the great hall 3 times out of 10 and in the servant's chamber less than 1 time out of 10—in fact, only once in each 25 times the game is played.

Answers to Problem 3.1 Follow-Up

See page 40c.

Problem 3.2

Answer each question, and explain your reasoning.

A. You have just advanced to level 2 of Treasure Hunt. What is the probability that the treasure is hidden in one of the queen's servants' rooms? In one of the king's servants' rooms?

B. What is the probability that the treasure is hidden in the maid's room? In the steward's room?

C. If you play the second level 100 times, how many times can you expect the treasure to be hidden in one of the queen's servants' rooms? In one of the king's servants' rooms?

D. If you play the second level 100 times, how many times can you expect the treasure to be hidden in the maid's room? In the steward's room?

▨ Problem 3.2 Follow-Up

1. You have just advanced to level 2. What is the probability that the treasure is hidden in one of the rooms on the second floor? Explain how you determined your answer.

2. You have just advanced to level 2. What is the probability that the treasure is hidden in the cook's room? Explain how you determined your answer.

Answers to Problem 3.2

A. See page 40c.   B. See page 40c.

C. Out of 100 times, the treasure can be expected to be hidden in one of the queen's servants' rooms about 50 times and in one of the king's servants' rooms about 50 times.

D. Out of 100 times, the treasure can be expected to be hidden in the maid's room about 25 times and in the steward's room about 17 times.

Answers to Problem 3.2 Follow-Up

1. 1; In level 2, the treasure *must* be hidden on the second floor.

2. 0; There is no cook's room on the second floor.

Answers

Applications

1a. Choose the king's rooms, as they occupy the greatest area.

1b. The queen's rooms occupy 8 + 4 + 4 + 10 + 4 = 30 squares of area, the princess's rooms occupy 3 + 4 + 3 = 10 squares of area, and the king's rooms occupy 100 – 40 = 60 squares of area. If level 3 were played 100 times, you could expect the treasure to be in the king's rooms about 60 times, the queen's rooms about 30 times, and the princess's rooms about 10 times.

1c. You could expect the treasure to be in the playroom about 3 out of 100 times.

As you work on these ACE questions, use your calculator whenever you need it.

Applications

1. The diagram below shows level 3 of the Treasure Hunt game. Before receiving the first clue, a player must guess whether the treasure is in a room used by the king, a room used by the queen, or a room used by the princess. When the treasure is actually located, a player receives bonus points if his or her initial guess was correct.

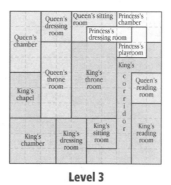

Level 3

a. Suppose you have just entered level 3. To have the best chance of getting the bonus points, should you guess that the treasure is in one of the king's rooms, one of the queen's rooms, or one of the princess's rooms? Give the reasons for your choice.

b. If you played this level 100 times, how many times would you expect the treasure to be in one of the king's rooms? In one of the queen's rooms? In one of the princess's rooms?

c. If you played this level 100 times, how many times would you expect the treasure to be in the princess's playroom?

In 2–4, use the dartboard shown to answer parts a–c.

2. **3.** **4.**

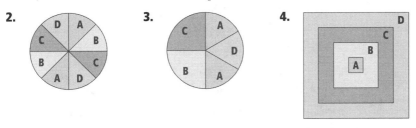

a. If a dart is thrown randomly at the board, what is the probability that it will land in a region marked A? In a region marked B? In a region marked C? In a region marked D?

b. The board is used to play a four-person game. Darts are thrown randomly at the board. Player A receives points when a dart lands in a region marked A, Player B receives points when a dart lands in a region marked B, and so on. Make up a scoring system that would make the game fair.

c. Using your point scheme from part b, what would you expect the score to be after 100 darts have been thrown?

5. Sarah, the designer of the Treasure Hunt game, considered several different floor plans for level 1. Here are two floor plans she rejected. Use these floor plans to answer parts a–d on the next page.

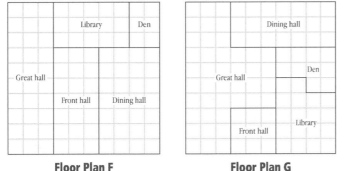

Floor Plan F **Floor Plan G**

2a. $P(A) = \frac{1}{4}$, $P(B) = \frac{1}{4}$, $P(C) = \frac{1}{4}$, $P(D) = \frac{1}{4}$

2b. Possible answer: Assign each region 1 point.

2c. 25 points for each player

3a. $P(A) = \frac{1}{3}$, $P(B) = \frac{1}{4}$, $P(C) = \frac{1}{4}$, $P(D) = \frac{1}{6}$

3b. Possible answer: Assign 3 points to region A, 4 points each to regions B and C, and 6 points to region D.

3c. Player A: about 33 × 3 = 99 points, Players B and C: 25 × 4 = 100 points, Player D: about 17 × 6 = 102 points

4a. $P(A) = \frac{1}{49}$, $P(B) = \frac{8}{49}$, $P(C) = \frac{16}{49}$, $P(D) = \frac{24}{49}$

4b. Possible answer: Assign 48 points to region A, 6 points to region B, 3 points to region C, and 2 points to region D.

4c. Player A: about 2 × 48 = 96 points, Player B: about 16 × 6 = 96 points, Player C: about 33 × 3 = 99 points, Player D: about 49 × 2 = 98 points

Investigation 3: Probability and Area **37**

5a. $\frac{15}{100}$

5b. $\frac{18}{100}$

5c. 15 times

5d. 18 times

Connections

6. The data more closely match floor plan F. The library and front hall had the treasure the same number of times, which is less likely to happen with floor plan G. The dining hall had the treasure only once more than the front hall, which is more likely to happen with floor plan F. Additionally, the great hall had the treasure only twice more than the front hall, and the two rooms are closer in size in floor plan F.

7. The probabilities would not be affected. The dimensions all increase by the same scale factor, so the ratio of each room's area to the total area will remain the same.

a. If level 1 had floor plan F, what would be the probability that the computer would hide the treasure in the library?

b. If level 1 had floor plan G, what would be the probability that the computer would hide the treasure in the library?

c. If level 1 had floor plan F, how many times out of 100 would you expect the computer to hide the treasure in the library?

d. If level 1 had floor plan G, how many times out of 100 would you expect the computer to hide the treasure in the library?

Connections

6. Sarah tested one of the floor plans from question 5. She kept track of the number of times the treasure was hidden in each room and made a bar graph of the results. Which floor plan do you think she was testing? Explain your reasoning.

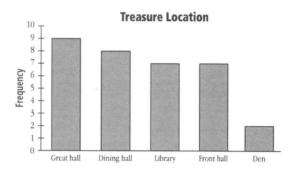

Treasure Location

7. If Sarah had enlarged floor plan F in question 5 by a scale factor of 2 to make a similar floor plan, how would this affect the probabilities?

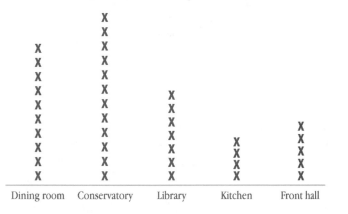

8. Rich, the programmer of the Treasure Hunt game, tested an early version of the level 1 floor plan. He kept track of the number of times the computer hid the treasure in each room, and he made a line plot of his results:

Because of a computer disk error, Rich has no record of the floor plan he was using. Design a floor plan that you would expect to give these data. State the area of each room on your floor plan.

Extensions

9. Create a floor plan for level 4 of the Treasure Hunt game. The floor should have five rooms, and the largest room should have the same area as the other four rooms combined. Label each room, and give its area.

---

8. Drawings will vary. According to the data, Rich played the game 38 times, and the experimental probabilities that the treasure will be in each room are as follows: P(dining room) = $\frac{10}{38} \approx 0.26$, P(conservatory) = $\frac{12}{38} \approx 0.32$, P(library) = $\frac{7}{38} \approx 0.18$, P(kitchen) = $\frac{4}{38} \approx 0.11$, P(front hall) = $\frac{5}{38} \approx 0.13$. On a 10 by 10 grid, the dining room should occupy about 26 squares, the conservatory about 32 squares, the library about 18 squares, the kitchen about 11 squares, and the front hall about 13 squares.

Extensions

9. See below left.

---

9. Drawings will vary. The largest room should have an area of $\frac{1}{2}$; and the four remaining rooms, combined, should have an area of $\frac{1}{2}$. Two possibilities:

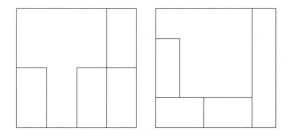

Possible Answers

1. When probabilities are related to area, two events that are represented by the same area are equally likely.

2. From the diagram, you find the part of the area occupied by that room and the total area of the rooms on that level and form a fraction:

$$P(\text{room}) = \frac{\text{area of room}}{\text{area of entire level}}$$

That fraction will give you the probability that the treasure will be hidden in that room.

(Note: It is important to understand that the total region needs to be thought of as having an area of 1. Then, the fractional areas of the parts can be thought of as corresponding to the probabilities of arriving at those outcomes. Sometimes an outcome can be represented by several different parts—showing that there may be more than one way to arrive at or to get a specific outcome—so you may have to add the fractions that represent the areas of the parts to find the probability of the outcome.)

Mathematical Reflections

In this investigation, you solved problems about games of chance in which probabilities were related to area. These questions will help you summarize what you have learned:

1 In games like Treasure Hunt in which probabilities are related to area, how can you tell if two events are equally likely?

2 In the Treasure Hunt game, how can you use the diagram of a level to find the probability that the treasure will be hidden in a particular room?

Think about your answers to these questions, discuss your ideas with other students and your teacher, and then write a summary of your findings in your journal.

Tips for the Linguistically Diverse Classroom

Original Rebus The Original Rebus technique is described in detail in *Getting to Know Connected Mathematics*. Students make a copy of the text before it is discussed. During the discussion, they generate their own rebuses for words they do not understand; the words are made comprehensible through pictures, objects, or demonstrations. Example: Question 2—Key phrases for which students might make rebuses are *diagram of a level* (sketch of a floor plan), *probability* (0 to 1), *treasure* (treasure box).

3.1 • Cracking Level 1

This problem introduces students to the idea of using area to evaluate theoretical probabilities. In the context of a computer game, students attempt to find a treasure hidden in one of the rooms of the first floor of a palace, which is laid out on a 10 by 10 grid.

Launch

It is not absolutely essential that students play the computer version of the game; they can analyze the game and investigate the probabilities without access to a computer. However, the game will be more intriguing to students if they actually play it. If students have access to computers outside of class, you might want to share copies of the game with them to use on their own.

Talk with the class about the Treasure Hunt game and how the computer hides the treasure. If you have a demonstration computer and the program, play a trial game with the class.

Pose the question in the "Think about this!" box preceding Problem 3.1, and ask students to share their explanations for their choice. Some may suggest that the areas of the rooms should be considered in guessing in which room the treasure is hidden. At this point, just have students share their ideas.

Have students work in groups of two or three on the problem, playing the computer game first if it is available.

Explore

To answer the questions, students will need to analyze the probabilities using the area model pictured in the student edition.

Have groups move on to the follow-up as soon as they are satisfied that they have correctly analyzed level 1 of the Treasure Hunt game.

Summarize

Discuss the questions posed in the problem, which ask students to analyze the game and to find theoretical probabilities based on the areas of the rooms. Students should realize that, because the computer randomly chooses a square on the grid for hiding the treasure, larger rooms have a greater chance of containing the treasure. If possible, display the transparency of the floor plan on Transparency 3.1A as the class discusses the problem.

Discuss the follow-up questions, and have groups share their answers.

> Is the probability that the computer will hide the treasure in the library affected by what happened in the previous game? *(No; the computer does not "remember" what happened in the previous games.)*

> Is the treasure as likely to be hidden in the entrance corridor as in the great hall? *(No, because the entrance corridor occupies less space.)*

What room is the most likely to hold the treasure? The next most likely? The next most likely? Which room is the least likely to hold the treasure? Explain your answers.

This summary can lead directly into the launch of Problem 3.2.

3.2 • Cracking Level 2

This problem introduces students to the idea that they can find probabilities of the treasure being hidden in any one of a given number of rooms by combining the areas of the rooms.

Launch

The summary of Problem 3.1 will lead into the launch of this problem. Read through Problem 3.2 with the class, verifying that students recognize that the floor plan is not drawn on a grid.

Is it equally likely that the treasure will be hidden in the maid's room as in the chancellor's room? Why or why not?

Have students work in their groups from Problem 3.1 to explore the problem and follow-up.

Explore

Because the king's servants' rooms and queen's servants' rooms each occupy half the floor space, students should easily be able to find the probability that the treasure will be hidden in these combinations of rooms. Finding the probability that the treasure is hidden in a single room will be more difficult because the rooms are not all the same size. Students will have to divide the floor plan into a grid visually, or copy the floor plan and find a way to divide it (a 10 by 12 grid will work). Have grid paper available for students who want to use it.

Use this opportunity to work with any students who are still having trouble using area to assign probabilities.

Summarize

Have students share their solutions to the questions, allowing time for them to explain how they determined the probability that the treasure will be hidden in a specific room or rooms. As students share their methods, ask if others agree and if they found the probabilities using the same method. You may want to use Transparency 3.2C during this discussion; it shows the level 2 floor plan on a 10 by 12 grid.

For part D, have students explain how they decided how many times out of 100 the treasure can be expected to be hidden in the steward's room. Each of the king's servants' rooms has a $\frac{1}{6}$ probability of containing the treasure, and $\frac{1}{6}$ of 100 is about 16.7. For students who say 17 (or 16) times, ask the following question:

What is 17 + 17 + 17? (51) Does this agree with how many times out of 100 we said the treasure should be in one of the king's servants' rooms?

In answering this, students must reflect on the consequences of working with rounded numbers. The treasure cannot be found in the room a fractional number of times, but the rounded number 16.7 suggests "about" 16 or 17 times. This idea is related to the concept of expected value, or long-term average, which is introduced more formally in Investigation 4.

In the follow-up, students revisit the ideas of 0 and 1 as probabilities. For some students, this will be a quick review; others may still be trying to make sense of what these two probabilities mean.

Additional Answers

Answers to Problem 3.1 Follow-Up

1. The probability that the treasure is hidden in the library is $\frac{12}{100}$, or 0.12, regardless of whether the treasure was in the library on the previous game.

2. Monty is incorrect. The entrance corridor has a probability of $\frac{6}{100}$, or 0.06, of being selected; the great hall has a probability of 0.30 of being selected. Although each square in the 10 by 10 grid has an equally likely chance of being chosen, each room does not because the rooms contain different numbers of squares.

Answers to Problem 3.2

A. The queen's servants' rooms occupy half the area of the second floor, so the probability that the treasure is hidden in one of them is $\frac{1}{2}$. The probability that the treasure is hidden in one of the king's servants' rooms is also $\frac{1}{2}$.

B. The maid's room occupies half the area of the queen's servants' rooms, or one fourth of the second floor, so the probability that the treasure is hidden in the maid's room is $\frac{1}{4}$. Likewise, the probability that the treasure is hidden in the steward's room is $\frac{1}{6}$.

Analyzing
Two-Stage Games

The first three investigations in this unit concern probabilities of *independent events*. For example, the outcome of tossing one coin is independent of the outcome of tossing a second coin. In this investigation, students encounter probability situations in which one event depends on another event, and they use an area model to analyze the probabilities of two or more such *dependent events*. In these problems, the outcomes are not equally likely, so a simple listing of the possible outcomes will not work. As you work through Investigations 4 and 5, look for opportunities to help students see the computational strategies that the area model supports. The teaching notes will help clarify the underlying mathematics.

In Problem 4.1, Choosing Paths, students analyze a maze that starts at a common point and terminates in one of two rooms. Students first simulate the game and analyze it using their simulation. Then, they use an area model to represent the probabilities of selecting the various paths. In Problem 4.2, Finding the Best Arrangement, students analyze a game that involves selecting one of two containers and then choosing a marble from the selected container. The challenge is to arrange two orange and two blue marbles in the two containers to maximize the probability of drawing an orange marble.

Mathematical and Problem-Solving Goals

- **To use an area model to represent the probability of two or more dependent events**

- **To solve problems by determining the probabilities of two or more dependent events**

Materials		
Problem	**For students**	**For the teacher**
All	Graphing calculators, grid paper (optional; provided as a blackline master)	Transparencies 4.1 and 4.2 (optional), transparent grids (optional; copy the grids onto transparency film)
4.1	Spinners, colored blocks, coins, and number cubes	
4.2	Colored blocks or other manipulatives (2 of each of 2 colors per group), opaque containers large enough for a student's hand (2 identical containers per group)	

INVESTIGATION

Analyzing Two-Stage Games

In the Treasure Hunt game and in games involving spinners and dartboards, you used area to find probabilities. In this investigation, you will learn how to use area in a slightly different way to analyze more situations involving probability.

4.1 Choosing Paths

Kenisha designed a computer game called Deep in the Dungeon. The game pits a player against a computer character named Zark. The game screen is shown below.

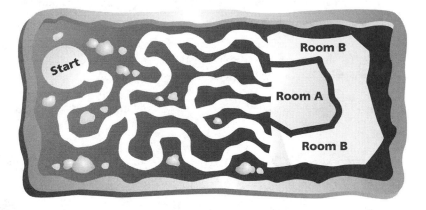

The player puts the treasure in one of the two rooms in the dungeon. Zark begins at "start" and makes his way toward the dungeon, *randomly* selecting a path at each fork. If Zark ends in the room with the treasure, he wins. If he ends in the room without the treasure, the player wins.

At a Glance

Grouping:
Groups of 2 or 4

Launch

- Introduce the Deep in the Dungeon game, and ask the class how they might simulate Zark *randomly* choosing paths.

- Play a game with the class, letting half the class hide the treasure and the other half proceed through the maze, randomly choosing paths.

Explore

- Circulate as groups work, asking questions that highlight the differences between these multistage outcomes and single-stage outcomes.

Summarize

- Discuss strategies for choosing paths and assigning experimental probabilities.

- As a class, pool the data and find the overall experimental probabilities.

- Do the follow-up as a class.

Assignment Choices

ACE questions 1, 4, 7, and unassigned choices from earlier problems

Problem 4.1

A. If you were playing Deep in the Dungeon, in which room would you put the treasure in order to have the best chance of beating Zark? Explain your choice.

B. Work with a partner to find a way to simulate Deep in the Dungeon so it can be played without a computer. Your simulation should be a two-person game. One person should hide the treasure, and the other should play the role of Zark. You will need to figure out a way for Zark to make a random selection at each fork.

C. Play your simulation of Deep in the Dungeon 20 times with your partner. Take turns hiding the treasure and playing Zark. For each game, record the room that Zark ends in.

D. Based on your results from part C, what is the experimental probability that Zark will end in room A? What is the experimental probability that Zark will end in room B?

■ **Problem 4.1 Follow-Up**

You and your classmates may have found several ways to simulate Deep in the Dungeon in order to find experimental probabilities. How could you determine the theoretical probabilities of Zark ending in each room?

One way to find the theoretical probabilities is by using an *area model*. To make it easier to talk about the game, we'll number the paths as shown below.

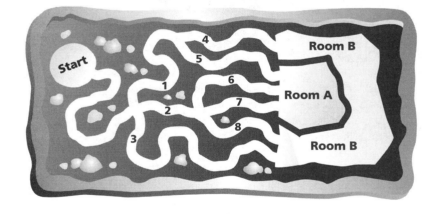

Answers to Problem 4.1

A. Possible answers: Room A because it is smaller. Either room because they each have three paths leading to them. Room B because the lowest path goes right to it.

B. Simulations will vary. See the Explore section for several ways to simulate the game.

C. Results will vary.

D. Answers will vary. Combining the entire class's data should bring the experimental probabilities close to $\frac{7}{18}$ for room A and $\frac{11}{18}$ for room B.

Answers to Problem 4.1 Follow-Up

See the Summarize section for an example of how to use an area model to represent the game. The theoretical probability that Zark will end in room A is $\frac{7}{18}$; the theoretical probability that he will end in room B is $\frac{11}{18}$.

1. Draw a square on your paper. Suppose that the square has an area of 1 square unit, representing a probability of 1. At the first fork, there are three equally likely choices: path 1, path 2, and path 3. Divide and label the square so the areas of the sections represent the probabilities of these three choices.

2. If Zark selects path 1 at the first stage of his journey, he will reach a fork where he must randomly select path 4 or path 5. Subdivide your diagram to represent the probabilities that Zark will choose path 1 and then choose path 4 or path 5.

3. If Zark selects path 2 at the first stage of his journey, he will reach a fork where he must randomly select path 6, path 7, or path 8. Subdivide your diagram to represent the probabilities that Zark will choose path 2 and then choose path 6, path 7, or path 8.

4. On your diagram, color the sections that represent paths leading to room A with one color and the sections that represent paths leading to room B with a second color.

5. What is the theoretical probability that Zark will end in room A? What is the theoretical probability that he will end in room B?

4.2 Finding the Best Arrangement

Brianna and Emmanuel are selected from the studio audience of the Gee Whiz Everyone Wins! game show to play a game. While Emmanuel waits backstage, Brianna is to place two orange marbles and two blue marbles in two identical containers in any way she chooses. After she places the marbles in the containers, Emmanuel will return and select one of the containers at random. Then, without looking, he will reach into the container and pull out a marble. If he draws an orange marble, the friends each win a prize. If he draws a blue marble, or if the container he chooses is empty, the friends do not win anything.

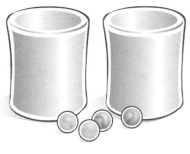

Tips for the Linguistically Diverse Classroom

Enactment The Enactment technique is described in detail in *Getting to Know Connected Mathematics*. Students act out mini-scenes using props to make information comprehensible. Example: When presenting "Finding the Best Arrangement," ask students to play the roles of Brianna and Emmanuel on the Gee Whiz Everyone Wins! game show. Orange and blue marbles or blocks and two identical, opaque containers can serve as props.

At a Glance

Grouping: Small Groups

Launch

- Introduce the game that Brianna and Emmanuel will play, and have students generate one way the marbles could be arranged.

- Have small groups investigate the problem.

Explore

- Suggest an area analysis to groups who are having trouble finding all the arrangements.

- As you circulate, ask for updates on how groups are thinking about the problem.

Summarize

- Have groups share the marble arrangements they found until all five have been discussed.

- Talk about how groups analyzed the arrangements, and present an area model if no group suggests one.

- Have groups do the follow-up, then discuss the answers.

Assignment Choices

ACE questions 2, 3, 5, 6, and unassigned choices from earlier problems

Problem 4.2

A. List all the different ways Brianna can place the four marbles in the two containers.

B. Which arrangement will give Brianna and Emmanuel the best chance of winning? Explain why the arrangement you chose is the best.

C. For the arrangement you chose, what is the probability of drawing an orange marble?

▨ Problem 4.2 Follow-Up

1. Which arrangement gives Brianna and Emmanuel the worst chance of winning?
2. Brianna and Emmanuel lost the first game but were given a chance to play a second game. This time Brianna had to place three orange marbles and three blue marbles in three containers. Find the arrangement that gives Emmanuel the best chance of drawing an orange marble.

Answers to Problem 4.2

A. See page 49k.   B. See page 49k.

C. The probability of drawing orange from the arrangement of one orange marble in one container and the three other marbles in the second container is $\frac{2}{3}$.

Answers to Problem 4.2 Follow-Up

1. The arrangement of all four marbles in one container gives them the worst chance of winning. The probability of drawing an orange marble with this arrangement is only $\frac{1}{4}$.

2. The best arrangement is one orange marble in one container, one orange marble in the second container, and one orange and three blue marbles in the third container. The probability of drawing an orange marble with this arrangement is $\frac{1}{3} + \frac{1}{3} + \frac{1}{12} = \frac{3}{4}$.

As you work on these ACE questions, use your calculator whenever you need it.

Applications

1. Kenisha created a new screen for Deep in the Dungeon.

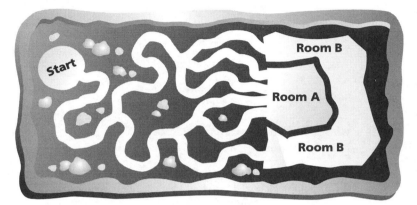

a. If Zark randomly selects a path at each fork, what is the theoretical probability that he will end in room A? In room B?

b. If you played this game 100 times, how many times would you expect Zark to end in room A? In room B?

2. Suppose Brianna (from Problem 4.2) was given three blue marbles and two orange marbles to distribute between the two containers. What arrangement would give Emmanuel the best chance of drawing an orange marble?

3. Suppose Brianna (from Problem 4.2) was given two blue marbles and three orange marbles to distribute between the two containers. What arrangement would give Emmanuel the best chance of drawing an orange marble?

---

3. The best arrangement is one orange marble in one container and the remaining marbles in the other container. As shown below, the probability of choosing orange is $\frac{3}{4}$.

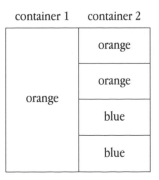

Answers

Applications

1a. A square can be divided to show the probability of Zark ending in each room. The theoretical probability of Zark ending in room A is $\frac{1}{6} + \frac{1}{6} + \frac{1}{8} + \frac{1}{8} = \frac{7}{12}$ and in room B is $\frac{1}{6} + \frac{1}{4} = \frac{5}{12}$.

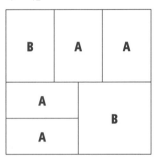

1b. If you played the game 100 times, you could expect Zark to end in room A $100 \times \frac{7}{12} =$ about 58 times and in room B $100 \times \frac{5}{12} =$ about 42 times.

2. The best arrangement is one orange marble in one container and the remaining marbles in the other container. A square can be divided to show that the probability of drawing orange is $\frac{5}{8}$.

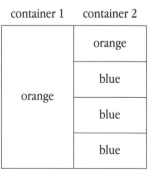

3. See left.

4a. The probability of ending in room A is $\frac{1}{6} + \frac{1}{12} + \frac{1}{12} = \frac{1}{3}$. The probability of ending in room B is $\frac{1}{6} + \frac{1}{3} + \frac{1}{12} + \frac{1}{12} = \frac{2}{3}$.

4b. See below right.

4. Kenisha designed a new version of Deep in the Dungeon with a different arrangement of paths and doors leading into rooms A and B. She made the area model below to analyze the probabilities of landing in each room.

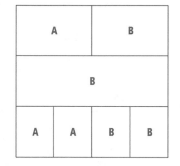

a. For Kenisha's new version, what is the probability that Zark will end up in room A? In room B?

b. Draw a game screen showing the paths, forks, and rooms that represents Kenisha's area model.

Connections

5. The table below shows the results of a survey that asked 100 seniors at Spartan High School the following questions:

- Do you favor a rule that would allow only seniors to drive to school?

- Do you drive to school?

Driving Survey

	Drives to school	Does not drive to school	Row totals
Favors rule	40	30	70
Opposes rule	20	10	30
Column total	**60**	**40**	**100**

4b. Game screens will vary. The first fork should break into three paths. One of those paths should lead to two paths (the upper route in the diagram shown here), one should lead directly to room B (the middle route), and one should lead to four paths (the lower route). The paths should enter the rooms as shown here.

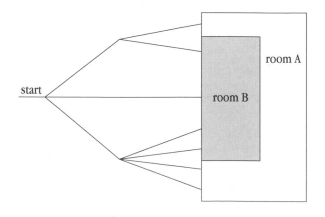

a. Based on this survey, what is the probability that a Spartan senior, selected at random, favors the rule?

b. What is the probability that a Spartan senior, selected at random, drives to school *and* favors the rule?

c. What is the probability that a Spartan senior, selected at random, drives to school *or* opposes the rule?

d. Do you think the results of this survey are a good indicator of how all the students at Spartan High School feel about the driving rule? Explain.

6. A bag contains three orange marbles and two blue marbles. You are to choose a marble, return it to the bag, and then choose again.

a. Tell whether each method below is appropriate for finding the possible outcomes of this experiment. If the method is appropriate, explain how you would use it to find the possible outcomes. If the method is not appropriate, explain why.

   i. making a counting tree
   ii. making a list
   iii. using an area model
   iv. making a table or chart

b. If you did this experiment 100 times, how many times would you expect to draw two marbles of the same color?

c. Suppose this experiment were a two-person game in which one player scores if the marbles match, and one player scores if they do not match. Describe a scoring system that would make this a fair game.

Connections

5a. As 70 of the 100 seniors surveyed favor the rule, the probability is $\frac{70}{100}$.

5b. As 40 of the 100 seniors surveyed drive to school and favor the rule, the probability is $\frac{40}{100}$.

5c. Of the 100 seniors surveyed, 60 drive to school. Of those who don't drive to school, 10 oppose the rule. This is a total of 70, so the probability is $\frac{70}{100}$. (Note: Adding the total number of seniors who drive to school, 60, to the total number who oppose the rule, 30, is incorrect because it double counts those who drive to school and oppose the rule.) Another way to do this problem is to determine who is *not* counted— seniors who do not drive to school and who favor the rule—a total of 30, which leaves 70.

5d. One problem with this survey is that it polled only seniors. Since the question concerns a rule that would allow only seniors to drive, many of the other students at Spartan might oppose it. Thus this survey is probably not a good indicator of the opinions of the entire student body.

6. See page 49k.

Extensions

7. The greatest chance of winning is in spinning spinner B twice. Possible explanation: The charts below right show that each way to spin the spinners results in two red-blue pairs; the way with the fewest possible outcomes is the best choice.

Extensions

7. At the school carnival, you are about to play a game using the two spinners below. You get two spins. You may spin each spinner once, or you may spin one of the spinners twice. If you get a red on one spin and a blue on the other spin (the order makes no difference), you win. To have the greatest chance of winning, should you spin spinner A twice, spin spinner B twice, or spin each spinner once? Explain how you got your answer.

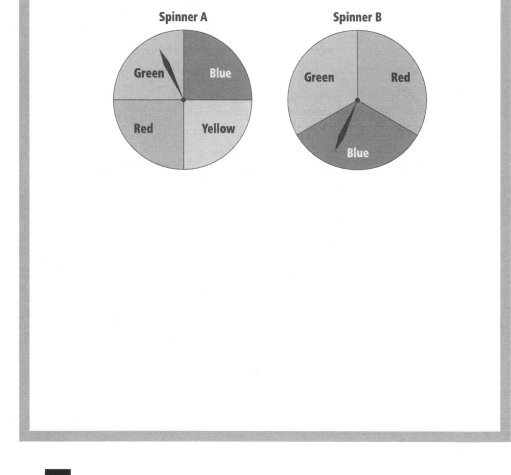

Spinning spinner A twice

	G	B	Y	R
G	GG	GB	GY	GR
B	BG	BB	BY	BR
Y	YG	YB	YY	YR
R	RG	RB	RY	RR

$$P(\text{winning}) = \tfrac{1}{8}$$

Spinning spinner B twice

	G	R	B
G	GG	GR	GB
R	RG	RR	RB
B	BG	BR	BB

$$P(\text{winning}) = \tfrac{2}{9}$$

Spinning both spinners

	G	R	B
G	GG	GR	GB
B	BG	BR	BB
Y	YG	YR	YB
R	RG	RR	RB

$$P(\text{winning}) = \tfrac{1}{6}$$

Mathematical Reflections

In this investigation, you analyzed probabilities by dividing the area of a square. These questions will help you summarize what you have learned:

1 In what kinds of situations is it appropriate to find probabilities by dividing the area of a square? Give an example to illustrate your answer.

2 How can you use the area of a square to analyze a probability situation? Use an example to help explain your answer. At each stage, explain how you decide how to divide the square.

Think about your answers to these questions, discuss your ideas with other students and your teacher, and then write a summary of your findings in your journal.

Possible Answers

1. A square area model is appropriate when there are two or more steps in a situation because you can show the different stages. The square model helps when you are looking at situations that deal with dependent events—that is, where what is done on the second step depends on the results of the first step. For example, suppose you wanted to randomly choose a T-shirt to wear and then a cap to go with it. The choice of the T-shirt limits which caps you could choose because you want the colors to match. A square could be divided first to show the T-shirt choices and then to show the cap choices for each T-shirt.

2. See page 49l.

Tips for the Linguistically Diverse Classroom

Diagram Code The Diagram Code technique is described in detail in *Getting to Know Connected Mathematics*. Students use a minimal number of words and drawings, diagrams, or symbols to respond to questions that require writing. Example: Question 1—A student might answer this question by writing *Problems with two steps* and drawing a square and dividing its area to show the probabilities of randomly choosing a T-shirt from the available choices and then selecting a matching cap.

TEACHING THE INVESTIGATION

4.1 • Choosing Paths

In this problem, students are introduced to using an area model to compute probabilities in situations involving a sequence of actions. Before using the model, they are given an opportunity to create their own method for analyzing the game.

Launch

Introduce the Deep in the Dungeon game. If possible, display the game screen, which is shown on Transparency 4.1. Ask questions to help the class focus on the probabilities in the game.

> In which room would you put the treasure? Why?

Some students may say room A because it is smaller; some may say the rooms have an equal chance of being entered by Zark because three paths lead into each room; some may say room B because one of the first paths leads directly into this room. Explain that they will be testing their ideas in this problem.

> How could we simulate Zark walking through the maze and choosing paths at random? *Random* means that we can't choose paths by picking our favorite number or our favorite direction. At each fork, every path must have exactly the same probability of being chosen.

> What things might help us to generate random choices?

Help students to see that rolling number cubes, spinning spinners, tossing coins, and choosing colored blocks designated to represent the path options are some of the methods that could be used to generate random choices.

> Let's play a version of Deep in the Dungeon in our class. We'll let the left side of the room choose the room in which to put the treasure. The right side of the room will pretend to be Zark, walking through the maze and choosing paths at random.

Let the left side of the room decide in which room to hide the treasure.

> Now, the right side of the room will walk through the maze. At each fork, you must choose a path in such a way that each path has exactly the same probability of being selected.

Let students decide how to do this. For example, they might roll a number cube, using even and odd when there are two paths from which to choose; and the numbers 1 or 2, 3 or 4, and 5 or 6 when there are three paths from which to choose. Or, they might draw from three blocks of different colors for a choice of three paths, and toss a coin for a choice of two paths.

As students make their selections, demonstrate them at the board or overhead. To help students focus on the initial path choices, you may want to cover all but the first fork until they have made their first choice.

Play the game a couple of times or until everyone understands how it is played.

Have spinners, number cubes, colored blocks, and coins available for groups to use to generate random choices.

Explore

Have groups of two or four play the game 20 times and record their results. As groups work, ask questions about what they are discovering.

> Which room seems to have the greater probability of Zark entering it? What makes you think this?
>
> If Zark comes to a fork that splits into three paths, what probability does each path have of being selected?
>
> Suppose Zark's first choice is to take one of three paths, each of which is followed by a choice of two paths. What is the probability that Zark will take any given second path?

Summarize

Collect groups' strategies for walking the maze and making random path choices at each fork. Have them share the experimental probabilities they have assigned to each possible outcome.

Help the class to pool their experimental data and to calculate the experimental probabilities based on all the groups' trials. When the class works on the follow-up, in which they will use an area model to find the theoretical probabilities that Zark will end in each room, they can use their experimental results to assess whether the theoretical probabilities they have calculated seem reasonable.

Ask the following question, and give students a few minutes to brainstorm the answer.

> How could you find the theoretical probability that a random path will lead to room A?

Occasionally, a group will design a strategy that is based on an area analysis. If this happens, use it as an opportunity to proceed to a discussion of the follow-up. If no one suggests an area analysis, work on the follow-up after all students have had an opportunity to express their ideas.

Some students will probably suggest using a counting tree. If so, ask questions to help them understand why a counting tree would be difficult to use here: the outcomes in this problem are not equally likely.

In one class, several groups suggested making a counting tree. The teacher had them draw their counting trees on the board and asked them to explain their drawings and how they used them to determine the theoretical probabilities. One group drew this counting tree:

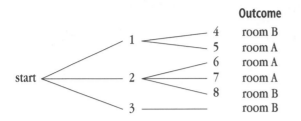

They explained that this counting tree shows that the theoretical probability of ending in room A is 50% and of ending in room B is 50% because it shows that there are six ways to get to the rooms and that three ways end in room A and three end in room B.

The teacher challenged their model by pointing out the discrepancy between their theoretical probabilities and the class's experimental probabilities. The class data did not support the idea that landing in either room was equally likely; instead, it indicated that Zark was more likely to end in room B if he made random choices. She added that although there were six different ways to get to the two rooms, not all seemed equally likely to be traveled. These comments were enough to make most students question the validity of the counting-tree approach they had used.

For the Teacher: Counting Trees

To use a counting-tree approach in a situation where outcomes are not equally likely, each branch of the tree must be weighted by the probability that it will be selected. This idea is quite difficult for students at this stage to understand; they have used counting trees only in situations involving equally likely outcomes. An area analysis makes the weighting more obvious. It is not recommended that you introduce this idea to your students now, but shown here is a counting tree that works.

Suppose the spinner from Problem 1.2 is spun twice. We can use a counting tree to find the possible outcomes and the probability of each.

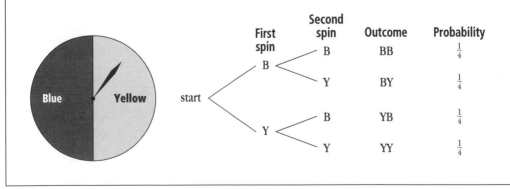

If we label the branches with the probabilities, we can see that by multiplying the probabilities, we get the same results.

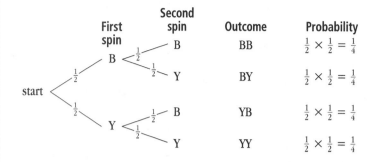

		Outcome	Probability
	BB	$\frac{1}{2} \times \frac{1}{2} = \frac{1}{4}$
	BY	$\frac{1}{2} \times \frac{1}{2} = \frac{1}{4}$
	YB	$\frac{1}{2} \times \frac{1}{2} = \frac{1}{4}$
	YY	$\frac{1}{2} \times \frac{1}{2} = \frac{1}{4}$

When the outcomes are not equally likely, we must label each branch and then multiply the probabilities along each path to obtain the correct results.

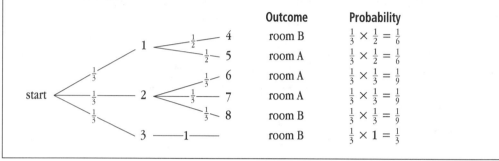

Outcome	Probability
room B	$\frac{1}{3} \times \frac{1}{2} = \frac{1}{6}$
room A	$\frac{1}{3} \times \frac{1}{2} = \frac{1}{6}$
room A	$\frac{1}{3} \times \frac{1}{3} = \frac{1}{9}$
room A	$\frac{1}{3} \times \frac{1}{3} = \frac{1}{9}$
room B	$\frac{1}{3} \times \frac{1}{3} = \frac{1}{9}$
room B	$\frac{1}{3} \times 1 = \frac{1}{3}$

As you work through the follow-up questions with the class, demonstrate subdividing a square as students draw their own area models at their desks. Question 1 asks students to divide and label a square to represent the probability of randomly selecting paths 1, 2, or 3 at the first fork. Because there are three choices, the square should be partitioned into three equal parts; for example:

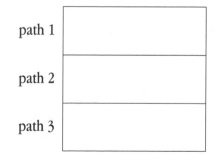

Path 1 is thus chosen with a probability of $\frac{1}{3}$. Proceeding along that path, you come to another fork with two paths.

Question 2 asks students to represent the two equally likely selections—paths 4 and 5—along the upper route. You might call on several students to demonstrate how this might be done. The area for path 1 should be divided into two equal parts to represent the two choices; for example:

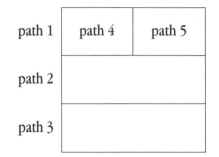

Help the class to analyze the drawing so far.

> What fraction of the total area of the square does each part of the upper route represent? *(Each part of the upper route occupies one sixth of the area.)*

Question 3 asks students to represent the three equally likely selections—paths 6, 7, and 8—along the middle route. The area for path 2 should be divided into three equal parts to represent the three choices. The area for path 3 requires no further subdivision.

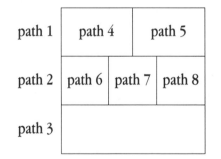

Question 4 asks students to color the sections representing paths leading to room A and those leading to room B differently; for example:

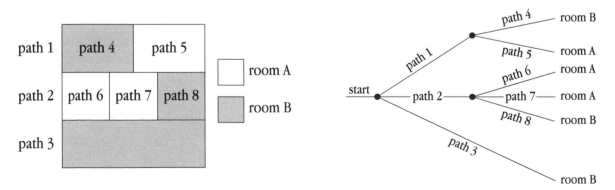

Question 5 asks students to use their area model to determine the theoretical probabilities of Zark ending in each room.

Now that we have divided a square to represent the different paths, what fraction should we assign to each part of our square?

The two parts representing the upper route are each $\frac{1}{6}$ of the square's area. The three parts representing the middle route are each $\frac{1}{9}$ of the square's area. The part representing the lower route is $\frac{1}{3}$ of the square's area.

These fractions represent the probabilities of Zark taking each series of paths.

What is the probability of Zark ending in room A? What is the probability of Zark ending in room B? How did you determine these probabilties?

Students can add the fractional parts of the square that represent ending in each room; for room A, $\frac{1}{6} + \frac{1}{9} + \frac{1}{9} = \frac{7}{18}$; for room B, $\frac{1}{6} + \frac{1}{9} + \frac{1}{3} = \frac{11}{18}$. Alternatively, they can continue to partition the square until all the parts are the same size:

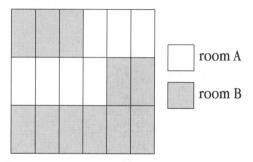

☐ room A

▨ room B

Of the 18 equal parts in the drawing, 7 represent room A, and 11 represent room B. Thus, P(room A) = $\frac{7}{18}$, and P(room B) = $\frac{11}{18}$.

If students present both of these ideas, point out that dividing the fractional parts of the square into parts of equal size is like finding a common denominator. The square above is divided into 18 equal parts. Since we were dealing with halves, thirds, thirds of halves (sixths), and thirds of thirds (ninths), we must use a grid that can easily show halves, thirds, sixths, and ninths. The common denominator of these fractions is 18.

Next, help students to apply the area model they have developed.

If you played Deep in the Dungeon 100 times, how many times would you expect Zark to end in room A? *(about 39 times)* In room B? *(about 61 times)*

If you played 100 times, how many times would you expect Zark to select path 1? *(about 33 times)* Path 4? *(about 17 times)* Path 6? *(about 11 times)*

How is our area model similar to the floor plans for the first and second floors of the palace in the Treasure Hunt game?

Students should see that in both situations, the fraction of the total area each room represents is the probability associated with that room. The difference is that the area model in this problem is based on the probabilities of selecting various paths.

To check whether students understand how to find the probabilities of successive events, draw another maze for the class to analyze. For example:

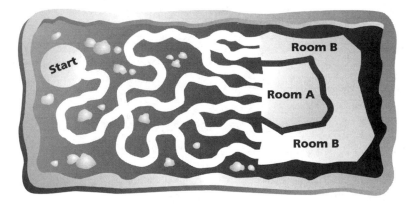

Give the class some time to think about this example. The associated area model for the example might look as follows:

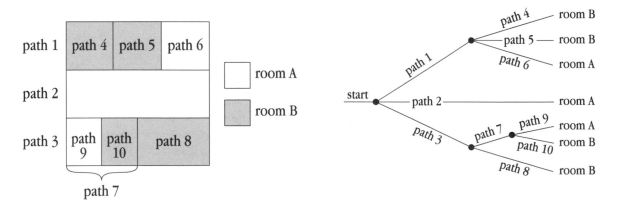

Adding the fractional parts of the drawing that represent ending in each room gives, for room A, $\frac{1}{9} + \frac{1}{3} + \frac{1}{12} = \frac{19}{36}$; and for room B, $\frac{1}{9} + \frac{1}{9} + \frac{1}{12} + \frac{1}{6} = \frac{17}{36}$.

4.2 • Finding the Best Arrangement

This problem gives students another chance to analyze two-stage games using an area model. This game involves dependent events. An area model allows students to focus on one stage, or decision, at a time. The second stage, or decision, is restricted as a portion of the total area. This is the equivalent of adjusting the sample space for the second stage to account for the result in the first stage.

Launch

Begin by telling the story of the game Brianna and Emmanuel are to play. Ask students for one way that two orange and two blue marbles could be arranged in two containers.

When students understand the game, have groups of three or four work on the problem. Each group will need two blocks, marbles, or other manipulatives in each of two colors and two identical opaque containers.

Explore

This is a difficult problem for students; they often struggle to find all the ways the four marbles can be arranged in two containers. Also, they may not see a relationship between this problem and Problem 4.1 and thus not realize that an area model is a reasonable way to find the theoretical probability of drawing an orange marble from each of the possible arrangements.

It is likely that many students will not initially realize that reversals of the contents of the two containers are not separate arrangements in a probabilistic sense. That is, the probability of drawing an orange marble when two blue marbles are in container 1 and two orange marbles are in container 2 is equal to the probability of drawing an orange marble when two blue marbles are in container 2 and two orange marbles are in container 1; there is no need to analyze both arrangements. Rather than pointing out that the containers are interchangeable and that these are equivalent situations, you may want to let students struggle with this idea, reach decisions about it within their groups, then clear up any misunderstanding during the summary.

As groups explore the problem, ask questions to help them make sense of their work.

> How do you know that you have considered all the possible ways to arrange the marbles in the containers?

If a group is really struggling with finding all the arrangements, model another arrangement with them.

> Once Brianna has put the marbles in the containers, what is the first choice that Emmanuel must make? *(He must select a container.)*

> What does Emmanuel do after he selects a container? *(He reaches in and, unless the container is empty, draws out a marble.)*

Think about the two choices Emmanuel has to make. What do you think is the probability of him drawing an orange marble in each of the arrangements? How might you show these two choices in your analysis?

Can you use what you learned in the last problem about area analysis to help you analyze this problem?

Summarize

Ask for all the ways the four marbles can be placed in the two containers. If students do not give all five arrangements (not counting reversals), say that you have another, and ask whether they can discover it. Putting all the marbles into one container is an arrangement students often miss.

Here are the five basic arrangements.

The associated theoretical probabilities of drawing an orange marble from each arrangement are as follows:

Container 1	2 orange	1 blue, 1 orange	1 blue, 2 orange	1 orange	—
Container 2	2 blue	1 blue, 1 orange	1 blue	2 blue, 1 orange	2 blue, 2 orange
P(orange)	$\frac{1}{2}$	$\frac{1}{2}$	$\frac{1}{3}$	$\frac{2}{3}$	$\frac{1}{4}$

Ask which arrangement will give Brianna and Emmanuel the best chance of winning. For each arrangement the groups suggest, have someone from that group illustrate on the board how they determined that it would give the friends the best chance of winning. If a particular group does not use an area analysis, ask another group to show how an area model could have been used to analyze that arrangement. If groups have other strategies, give them a chance to offer these for class consideration.

If no group presents an area model as a means of determining the theoretical probabilities for the various arrangements, demonstrate how to apply an area model to one of the arrangements. Some students have trouble understanding the probability of drawing an orange marble when all the marbles are placed in one container. You may want to work through this situation with the class.

Let's use an area model to represent putting all four marbles in one container. What is the first decision Emmanuel must make? *(He must select a container.)* How do we represent this with an area model?

A square could be drawn to represent the total probability, and it could be divided into two equal parts to represent the choice between the two containers. For example:

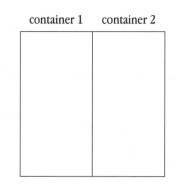

After selecting a container, what must Emmanuel do to complete the game?

Emmanuel must reach in and select a marble. If he chooses the empty container, when he reaches in he will get nothing.

How can we represent this step with our area model?

The region representing the container of four marbles—for example, container 1—must be divided into four equal parts, two for orange and two for blue. The region for the second container needs no further division.

container 1	container 2
orange	
orange	
blue	
blue	

Based on our area model, what is the probability of drawing an orange marble with this arrangement? ($\frac{1}{4}$) What is the probability of drawing a blue marble? ($\frac{1}{4}$) What is the probability of drawing nothing? ($\frac{1}{2}$)

Have groups work on follow-up question 1, which asks which arrangement gives the friends the *worst* chance of winning. Collect all ideas, again having students illustrate their analysis of each arrangement they suggest. If no one uses an area analysis, ask someone to show how an area model could be used.

Now, turn the class's attention to follow-up question 2. Let groups present their ideas about how to analyze the various options in this new game.

Additional Answers

Answers to Problem 4.2

A. Note: The probabilities are given here for reference. The containers can be reversed, but the probabilities for the arrangements remain the same.

Container 1	2 orange	1 blue, 1 orange	1 blue, 2 orange	1 orange	—
Container 2	2 blue	1 blue, 1 orange	1 blue	2 blue, 1 orange	2 blue, 2 orange
P(orange)	$\frac{1}{2}$	$\frac{1}{2}$	$\frac{1}{3}$	$\frac{2}{3}$	$\frac{1}{4}$

B. The arrangement of one orange marble in one container and the three other marbles in the second container gives them the best chance of winning. When we used a square to analyze this option, the area for orange was greater than in the other options.

ACE Answers

Connections

6a. Any of the methods could be used, though some might be easier to use than others.

i. To use a counting tree, five branches would represent the first draw. From each of these, another five branches would represent the second draw. This would result in 25 different outcomes.

ii. To use a list, you have to be careful to distinguish between the different orange and blue marbles (for example, by using symbols such as O_1, O_2, O_3, B_1, B_2). You would list O_1 with each of the other possibilities, and then O_2 with each of the other possibilities, and so on.

iii. To use an area model, you could divide a square into five columns to represent the first draw. Then, divide each column into five parts to represent the second draw.

iv. A chart would be similar to the area model, with five rows and five columns as shown here.

	O	O	O	B	B
O	OO	OO	OO	OB	OB
O	OO	OO	OO	OB	OB
O	OO	OO	OO	OB	OB
B	BO	BO	BO	BB	BB
B	BO	BO	BO	BB	BB

6b. Of the 25 possible outcomes, 13 represent marbles of the same color, so you could expect to draw two marbles of the same color $\frac{13}{25}$, or 52%, of the time, or 52 out of 100 times.

6c. Possible answer: Award 12 points for getting a match and 13 points for getting a no-match.

Mathematical Reflections

2. You can use the area of a square to represent 1, and the area representing each outcome is associated with a fractional part of the square. For example, suppose you have three T-shirts—red, blue, and green. You also have four baseball caps—a red and blue cap, a green and yellow cap, a red and yellow cap, and a blue and white cap. You will first randomly choose a T-shirt. Then, you will randomly choose a cap from those that contain a color that matches the shirt. You are wondering what the probability is that you will choose each possible combination.

First, you divide a square into three equal parts to represent the three shirt choices. Next, you need to determine the cap choices for each shirt. For the red shirt, there are two caps (red/blue and red/yellow); for the blue shirt, there are two caps (red/blue and blue/white). Each of these regions is divided in half. The green shirt corresponds to only one cap (green/yellow), so that region is not subdivided. The probability of choosing each cap can be found by adding its fractional areas. The red/blue cap has a probability of $\frac{1}{6} + \frac{1}{6} = \frac{1}{3}$, the red/yellow and blue/white caps each have a probability of $\frac{1}{6}$, and the green/yellow cap has a probability of $\frac{1}{3}$.

Red shirt	Blue shirt	Green shirt
R/B cap	R/B cap	
		G/Y cap
R/Y cap	B/W cap	

Expected Value

In this investigation, students continue using an area model to analyze dependent events, and they are formally introduced to the concept of *expected value,* or long-term average. Students have been working with this idea informally from the beginning of the unit. When they were making unfair games fair, for example, they were essentially making the expected values for each player equal.

In Problem 5.1, Shooting the One-and-One, students simulate a free-throw situation in basketball. In a one-and-one, a player attempts a shot from the free-throw line; if she makes it, she attempts a second. Taking a second shot *depends* on whether the player makes the first shot. Students then use an area model to find the associated theoretical probabilities. The question of what happens in the long run is raised in Problem 5.2, Finding Expected Value. If the player attempts a one-and-one 100 times, what would we expect her average points per trip to be? This *expected value* tells what the player could expect to average over many trials. Using an area model to analyze situations involving two or more dependent events makes the problems accessible to students. In addition, the analysis of the area model helps them to understand the underlying multiplication model.

Mathematical and Problem-Solving Goals

- **To determine the probability of an event that consists of a sequence of two independent outcomes in which the probability of the second outcome depends on the first outcome**

- **To understand how to use probabilities and equivalent fractions to find expected value**

- **To use area models and the concept of expected value to solve probability problems**

Materials

Problem	For students	For the teacher
All	Graphing calculators, 10 by 10 grids (optional; provided as blackline masters)	Transparencies 5.1A to 5.2 (optional), transparent 10 by 10 grid (optional)
5.1	Labsheet 5.1 (optional; 1 per 2 pairs), colored blocks, 10-sided number cubes	
5.2	Labsheet 5.2 (1 per pair), 10-section, 12-section, and 16-section spinners (optional; provided as blackline masters)	Transparency of Labsheet 5.2 (optional)

Student Pages 50–58   Teaching the Investigation 58a–58k

Launch

■ Tell the story of Nicky's one-and-one free-throw situation.

■ Work through parts A and B as a class, discussing how many points students think Nicky will score demonstrating the simulation methods students suggest.

Explore

■ Have pairs conduct a simulation and work on the remaining questions, and verify that pairs' simulations will correctly represent the situation.

■ Ask how the second shot is affected by, or depends on, the result of the first shot.

Summarize

■ Combine all the data, and talk about the remaining parts of the problem.

■ Have pairs do the follow-up.

Expected Value

On April 14, 1993, during half-time of a basketball game between the Chicago Bulls and the Miami Heat, Don Calhoun won 1 million dollars by making a basket from the free-throw line at the opposite end of the court. Don was chosen at random from the audience to attempt the shot as part of a promotional contest. A *Sports Illustrated* article explains:

> The odds against one randomly chosen person given one shot from the opposite foul line and making it are considered astronomical. Scottie Pippen admitted that after practice one day he and Michael Jordan tried to hit the shot but couldn't.*

Not every shot is this difficult to make! In this investigation, you will use a player's free-throw percentage to figure out what is likely to happen in a given free-throw situation.

5.1 Shooting the One-and-One

Nicky is playing basketball on her school team this year. In the district finals, the team is 1 point behind with 2 seconds left in the game. Nicky has just been fouled, and she is in a one-and-one free-throw situation. This means that Nicky will try one shot. If she makes the first shot, she gets to try a second shot. If she misses the first shot, she is done and does not get to try a second shot. Nicky's free-throw average is 60%.

Reprinted courtesy of Sports Illustrated:"Sports People: Don Calhoun" by Lisa Bessone, SI, April 26, 1993, Time Inc. All rights reserved.

50 **What Do You Expect?**

Assignment Choices

ACE questions 7–9 and unassigned choices from earlier problems

Answers to Problem 5.1

A. Answers will vary. Many students will guess that 1 point is the most likely result.

B. Plans will vary. Spinning a spinner, rolling a number cube, and drawing colored blocks from a container are three methods that might be used.

C. Answers will vary. One pair's simulation resulted in Nicky scoring 0 points 7 times, 1 point 5 times, and 2 points 8 times.

D. Answers will vary. For the data in part C, P(0 points) = $\frac{7}{20}$ = 35%, P(1 point) = $\frac{5}{20}$ = 25%, and P(2 points) = $\frac{8}{20}$ = 40%.

E. See page 58i.

F. See page 58i.

Problem 5.1

A. Which of the following do you think is most likely to happen?

- Nicky will score 0 points. That is, she will miss the first shot.
- Nicky will score 1 point. That is, she will make the first shot and miss the second shot.
- Nicky will score 2 points. That is, she will make two shots.

Record what you think before you analyze the situation.

B. Plan a way to simulate this situation. Describe your plan.

C. Use your plan from part B to simulate Nicky's one-and-one situation 20 times. Record the result of each trial.

D. Based on your results, what is the experimental probability that Nicky will score 0 points? That she will score 1 point? That she will score 2 points?

E. Make an area model for this situation, using a 10 by 10 grid. What is the theoretical probability that Nicky will score 0 points? 1 point? 2 points?

F. How do the three theoretical probabilities compare with the three experimental probabilities?

▧ Problem 5.1 Follow-Up

1. Suppose Nicky is in a two-shot free-throw situation. This means that she will get a second shot even if she misses the first shot. What is the theoretical probability that Nicky will score 0 points? That she will score 1 point? That she will score 2 points? Explain your reasoning.

2. How do the theoretical probabilities for the one-and-one situation compare to the theoretical probabilities for the two-shot situation?

5.2 Finding Expected Value

In the last problem, you looked at the probabilities of different outcomes of Nicky's one-and-one free-throw situation. You might have been surprised about which outcome is most likely. In this problem, you will look at the number of points Nicky can expect to make each time she is in a one-and-one free-throw situation.

Answers to Problem 5.1 Follow-Up

1. See page 58i.

2. The probability of scoring 2 points is unchanged because there is only one way to get 2 points, by making both shots. The probability of scoring 1 point is much greater in the two-shot situation, as there are two ways to score 1 point. Each way has a probability of 24 out of 100, or a total of 48 ways out of 100. The probability of 0 points is consequently greatly reduced. To get 0 points, Nicky must miss two shots in a row, which has a probability of $0.40 \times 0.40 = 0.16$, or 16%.

▪▪▪ At a Glance

Grouping: Whole Class, then Pairs

Launch

- Work through the problem as a class.

- Distribute Labsheet 5.2, and as a class, find the expected value for the 60% shooter.

Explore

- Have students work in pairs to complete the labsheet.

Summarize

- Review the labsheet, and ask students what patterns they see in the table.

- Talk about the expected values of the various free-throw shooters.

Assignment Choices

ACE questions 1–6, 10–13, and unassigned choices from earlier problems (10 by 10 grids may be helpful for some problems)

Assessment

It is appropriate to use Check-Up 2 after this problem.

Problem 5.2

Suppose Nicky has a 60% free-throw average and is in a one-and-one free-throw situation 100 times during the season.

A. What total number of points would you expect Nicky to score in these 100 trips to the free-throw line?

B. What would Nicky's average number of points per trip be? This is the **expected value** for this situation.

■ Problem 5.2 Follow-Up

Use Labsheet 5.2 to investigate what is likely to happen in one-and-one situations involving players whose free-throw averages are different from Nicky's. When you have finished the labsheet, use it to help you answer the following questions.

1. How do the probabilities of scoring exactly 1 point in a one-and-one situation compare for 20%, 40%, 60%, and 80% shooters? Describe any pattern you see in the table.

2. In a one-and-one situation, what is the most likely outcome for a 20% shooter? For a 40% shooter? For a 60% shooter? For an 80% shooter? How do these outcomes compare?

3. a. Make a graph that shows the average numbers of points a 20% shooter, a 40% shooter, a 60% shooter, and an 80% shooter can expect to make in a one-and-one situation. Use your graph to answer parts b–d.

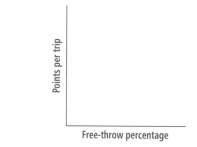

b. How do the expected values compare for a 20% shooter, a 40% shooter, a 60% shooter, and an 80% shooter?

c. Nicky's father noticed that he makes an average of about 1 point whenever he is in a one-and-one free-throw situation. What do you think his shooting percentage is?

d. If Nicky's twin sister Michelle is a 70% shooter, what is her expected value in a one-and-one situation? Check your answer by making an area model.

Answers to Problem 5.2

A. Nicky would score a total of 0 for the 40 times she expects to score 0 points, a total of 24 for the 24 times she expects to score 1 point, and a total of 72 for the 36 times she expects to score 2 points. This is an overall total of 0 + 24 + 72 = 96 points.

B. 96 points ÷ 100 trips = 0.96 point/trip

Answers to Problem 5.2 Follow-Up

See page 58i.

Applications • Connections • Extensions

As you work on these ACE questions, use your calculator whenever you need it.

Applications

1. a. Brian is a 50% free-throw shooter. In a one-and-one free-throw situation, is he most likely to score 0 points, 1 point, or 2 points? Explain your reasoning.

b. Over the long run, what is the average number of points Brian can expect to score per one-and-one situation? That is, what is his expected value?

2. Nicky, a 60% free-throw shooter, is in a two-shot free-throw situation. Remember, this means that she will attempt the second shot no matter what happens on the first shot.

a. Is Nicky most likely to score 0 points, 1 point, or 2 points? Explain your answer.

b. Nicky plans to keep track of her score on two-shot free-throw situations. What average number of points can she expect to score per two-shot situation?

3. Fred and Josephina are experimenting with a new game. They figure out that the probability Fred will win a round is $\frac{1}{3}$, and the probability Josephina will win a round is $\frac{2}{3}$. They decided that to make the game fair Fred should score 3 points when he wins a round, and Josephina should score 2 points when she wins a round.

a. If they play 12 rounds of the game, how many points can Fred expect to score? How many points can Josephina expect to score?

b. How many points per round can each player expect to score? That is, what is the expected value for each player?

c. Is this a fair game? Why or why not?

1a. As shown in the area model below, Brian is most likely to score 0 points.

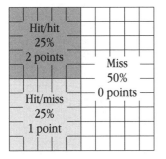

2a. As shown in the area model below, Nicky is most likely to score 1 point.

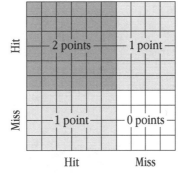

Answers

Applications

1a. See below left.

1b. In 100 attempts, Brian could expect to score 2 points 25 times, 1 point 25 times, and 0 points 50 times, for an overall total of 25(2) + 25(1) + 50(0) = 75 points. The average number of points he could expect per trip is thus 75 ÷ 100 = 0.75.

2a. See below left.

2b. In 100 attempts, Nicky could expect to score 2 points 36 times, 1 point 48 times, and 0 points 16 times, for an overall total of 36(2) + 48(1) + 16(0) = 120 points. The average number of points she could expect per trip is thus 120 ÷ 100 = 1.2.

3a. If they play the game 12 times, Fred could expect to win $\frac{1}{3} \times 12 = 4$ times and Josephina $\frac{2}{3} \times 12 = 8$ times. Fred can expect to score $3 \times 4 = 12$ points, and Josephina can expect to score $2 \times 8 = 16$ points.

3b. Fred can expect to score 12 ÷ 12 = 1 point per game, and Josephina can expect to score 16 ÷ 12 = about 1.33 points per game.

3c. This is not a fair game because Fred and Josephina do not have the same expected score per game.

4. David has the best chance of making his next free throw, as his percentage is the highest.

Player	Percent made
Gerrit	50%
David	79.6%
Ken	61.6%
Alex	70%

5. Students may want to use 10 by 10 grids to analyze these situations.

5a. **i.** P(0 points) = 30%
ii. P(1 point) = 21%
iii. P(2 points) = 49%

5b. **i.** 30 times
ii. 21 times
iii. 49 times

5c. If Alex goes to the free-throw line 100 times, he could expect to score 2 points 49 times, 1 point 21 times, and 0 points 30 times, for an overall total of 49(2) + 21(1) + 30(0) = 119 points. Thus, the average number of points he could expect per trip is 119 ÷ 100 = 1.19.

In 4–6, use the information in this table, which shows free-throw statistics for some of the players on Mr. Luft's basketball team.

Name	Free throws attempted	Free throws made
Gerrit	54	27
David	49	39
Ken	73	45
Alex	60	42

4. Which of the boys listed has the best chance of making his next free throw? Explain your reasoning.

5. **a.** Alex has just been fouled and is in a one-and-one free-throw situation. What is the probability of each of the following outcomes?

i. Alex will score 0 points. That is, he will miss the first shot.
ii. Alex will score 1 point. That is, he will make the first shot and miss the second shot.
iii. Alex will score 2 points.

b. If Alex is in a one-and-one situation 100 times, how many times would you expect each of the outcomes listed in part a to occur?

c. What is the average number of points you could expect Alex to make per one-and-one situation?

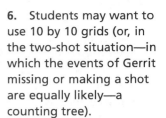

6. a. Suppose Gerrit is in a one-and-one free-throw situation. What is the probability of each of the following outcomes?

   i. Gerrit will score 0 points.
   ii. Gerrit will score 1 point.
   iii. Gerrit will score 2 points.

b. Suppose Gerrit is in a two-shot free-throw situation. What is the probability of each of the following outcomes?

   i. Gerrit will score 0 points.
   ii. Gerrit will score 1 point.
   iii. Gerrit will score 2 points.

c. Compare your answers to parts a and b. Explain why the answers to these two questions are not exactly the same.

Connections

7. The Wheel of Fortune® game show uses a large spinner with many sections. At least one section is labeled "bankrupt." If a player spins "bankrupt," she loses her turn and all her money. Luisa created her own version of the Wheel of Fortune spinner so she could play the game with her friends. Her spinner is shown here.

a. What is the probability that a player who spins this wheel one time will land on bankrupt?

b. What is the probability that a player who spins this wheel one time will get $500 or more?

c. Sam just spun the wheel and landed on $350. What is the probability he will land on $350 on his next spin? Explain your reasoning.

6. Students may want to use 10 by 10 grids (or, in the two-shot situation—in which the events of Gerrit missing or making a shot are equally likely—a counting tree).

6a. i. P(0 points) = 50%
ii. P(1 point) = 25%
iii. P(2 points) = 25%

6b. i. P(0 points) = 25%
ii. P(1 point) = 50%
iii. P(2 points) = 25%

6c. The probabilities for making both shots in the two situations are equal. The other two probabilities are different because in the two-shot situation Gerrit can score 1 point by either making the first shot and missing the second, or missing the first shot and making the second. He's twice as likely to score 1 point in the second situation than in the first, and half as likely to score 0 points.

Connections

7a. Each section is equally likely, so there is a 1 in 10, or 10%, chance of landing on bankrupt.

7b. Three of the 10 sections have a value of $500 or more, so the probability of getting at least $500 on one spin is $\frac{3}{10}$, or 30%.

7c. It is still 10%. Each player has a 10% chance of hitting $350 on each spin.

8a. See page 58k.

8b. According to Wanda's predictions, there was a 9% chance that it would rain on both days. Thus, while it was unlikely that it would rain both days, it was not impossible. Wanda's knowledge should not be in question just because she didn't predict something that had only a 9% chance of happening.

8c. See below right.

9a. The factors of 5 are 5 and 1, so there is a $\frac{1}{3}$ chance on each roll of getting a factor of 5. The probability of getting a factor of 5 on two consecutive rolls is $\frac{1}{9}$. (Note: Students may list all possible combinations, draw an area model, or if they are beginning to see the connection to multiplying fractions, compute $\frac{1}{3} \times \frac{1}{3} = \frac{1}{9}$.)

9b. $\frac{1}{9}$

9c. The answers are the same; rolling the same number cube a second time is equivalent to rolling a second number cube. Each roll of a number cube is independent of other rolls.

8. Wanda, the new Channel 1 weather reporter, said there was a 30% chance of rain on Saturday and a 30% chance of rain on Sunday. It rained both days, and Wanda's station manager is wondering if Wanda really knows how to predict weather.

a. Suppose Wanda had done all the calculations correctly, and according to her data there really was a 30% chance of rain each day. What was the probability that there would be rain on *both* days?

b. Do you think this incident means that Wanda doesn't know very much about predicting weather? Why or why not?

c. Wanda is working on her predictions for the next few days. She uses information from the weather satellite to calculate that there is a 20% chance of rain on Monday and a 20% chance of rain on Tuesday. If she is correct, what is the probability that it will rain on at least one of these days?

9. a. If you roll one number cube two times, what is the probability of getting a factor of 5 both times?

b. If you roll two different number cubes, what is the probability of getting a factor of 5 on both cubes?

c. How do your answers to parts a and b compare? Explain why the answers have this relationship.

8c. As shown in the area model below, there is a 36% chance that it will rain on at least one of the two days.

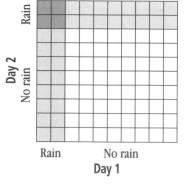

10. Mr. Maldonado brought his dog Scout to the vet for a pregnancy test. Since the test gives an accurate prediction only 80% of the time, the vet decides to test Scout twice.

a. If Scout is pregnant, what is the probability that both tests will say she is *not* pregnant? (It may help to use a 10 by 10 grid to make an area model of this situation.)

b. If Scout is pregnant, what is the probability that at least one of the tests will indicate that she *is* pregnant?

Extensions

In 11 and 12, use the data about Mr. Luft's basketball team from questions 4–6.

11. What is the probability that Alex will make his next three free throws? Explain your reasoning.

12. David is in a one-and-one free-throw situation. What is the probability that he will make both shots?

13. Regina has worked hard all season and has increased her shooting percentage to 50%. She tells her coach that she would like to be a starter for the rest of the games this season. The coach makes a deal with Regina. At tomorrow's practice, Regina can attempt either to make three shots in a row or to make at least four out of five shots. If Regina is successful, she will start every game for the rest of the season. Which option should Regina choose? Explain your reasoning.

---

13. The probability that Regina will make three shots in a row is $\frac{5}{10} \times \frac{5}{10} \times \frac{5}{10} = \frac{125}{1000}$, or about 13%. The probability that she will make at least four out of five shots is about 19% (see the explanation that follows), so Regina should go with this option. The probability that Regina will miss any one shot is 50% or 0.5, so the probability that she will miss her first shot and make the last four is $0.5 \times 0.5 \times 0.5 \times 0.5 \times 0.5 =$ about 0.0313, or 3.13%. This is the same probability that Regina will miss only the second shot, or miss only the third shot, and so on, for a combined probability of about $5 \times 3.13\% = 15.65\%$. There is also a $0.5 \times 0.5 \times 0.5 \times 0.5 \times 0.5 =$ about 3.13% chance that she could make all five shots. Thus, the total probability that Regina will make at least four out of five shots is $15.65\% + 3.13\% =$ about 18.8%.

10a. See page 58k.

10b. In the area model, 4 squares indicate two negative test results; the remaining 96 squares represent a positive test result. The probability that at least one test will indicate that Scout is pregnant is 96%.

Extensions

11. The probability that Alex will make one free throw is 70%, or $\frac{7}{10}$. Out of 100 sets of three free throws, he will make the first shot about 70% of the time, or 70 times. Out of those 70 times, he will make the second shot about 70% of the time, or $0.7 \times 70 = 49$ times. Out of those 49 times, he will make the third shot about 70% of the time, or $0.7 \times 49 =$ about 34 times. Thus, the probability that he will make his next three free throws is about 34%.

12. David's free-throw average is 79.6%, or about 80%. Out of 100 attempts, David can expect to make 80 of his first shots. Of his 80 second shots, he can expect to make the second free throw 80% of the time, or about 64 times. This gives him about a 64% chance of making both free throws. (Note: Students might also multiply probabilities: $\frac{39}{49} \times \frac{39}{49} = \frac{1521}{2401}$, or about 63.3%, of the time.)

13. See left.

Possible Answers

1. To calculate the probability of an outcome with more than one step, you could first show the probability of the first step on a grid of 100 squares, and then show how much the second probability occupies of the area covered by the first probability. For example, a 70% free-throw shooter in a one-and-one situation would make the first shot 70% of the time.

The shooter would then make 70% of the second shots.

The probability that he will make any specific number of points can be found using the area model:
P(0 points) = $\frac{30}{100}$ or 30%,
P(1 point) = $\frac{21}{100}$ or 21%,
and P(2 points) = $\frac{49}{100}$ or 49%.

2. See page 58k.

Mathematical Reflections

In this investigation, you learned how to find the average number of points a basketball player could expect to make per trip to the free-throw line. This average is the expected value for the situation. These questions will help you summarize what you have learned:

1 How would you calculate the probability of an outcome that has more than one step? Illustrate your answer by finding the probabilities of the possible outcomes for a 70% free-throw shooter in a one-and-one situation.

2 How would you calculate the expected value for a situation? Illustrate your answer by finding the average number of points per one-and-one situation for a 70% free-throw shooter.

Think about your answers to these questions, discuss your ideas with other students and your teacher, and then write a summary of your findings in your journal.

Tips for the Linguistically Diverse Classroom

Diagram Code The Diagram Code technique is described in detail in *Getting to Know Connected Mathematics*. Students use a minimal number of words and drawings, diagrams, or symbols to respond to questions that require writing. Example: Question 1—A student might answer this question by writing *First step* and shading a grid of 100 squares to show the probability of the first step in the proposed problem. Then, the student might write *Probability with both steps* and draw a second grid, this time also showing how much the second probability occupies the area covered by the first probability.

5.1 • Shooting the One-and-One

Most students find this problem difficult. What is likely to happen when Nicky attempts her shots is more difficult to analyze than it may first appear; thinking of ways to simulate the situation is challenging as well. (Shooting free throws is not a viable way to simulate the problem because people either do not know their averages or their averages vary. In reality, a free-throw shooter's average does not usually remain constant. To simplify the work in this unit, the underlying assumption is that a shooter's average remains constant.) Reproducible sheets of 10-section spinners are provided for students who want to use spinners to simulate probability situations.

Launch

Tell the story of Nicky's basketball game, or personalize a similar story using teams and players that would be of interest to your class. Make sure everyone understands what a *free throw* and a *one-and-one situation* are.

> What are the possible numbers of points that Nicky could score in a one-and-one situation? *(0 points, 1 point, or 2 points)*
>
> Explain how each of these can happen. *(She will score 0 points if she misses the first shot, 1 point if she makes the first shot but misses the second, and 2 points if she makes both shots.)*

The problem will probably proceed more smoothly if you work as a class on parts A and B, then have students explore the rest of the problem in pairs.

> Nicky's free-throw average is 60%. What do you think is most likely to happen: that she scores 0 points, 1 point, or 2 points? Explain your answer.

The intention of part A is for students to express their ideas, not to finalize an argument. You could have students vote on which result they think is most likely. Most will guess that Nicky will score 1 point and the game will end in a tie.

For the Teacher

A 60% free-throw shooter in a one-and-one situation is most likely to score 0 points and least likely to score 1 point. P(score, score) = 0.6 × 0.6 or 0.36; P(score, miss) = 0.6 × 0.4 or 0.24; P(miss) = 0.40.

> How might you figure out what is most likely to happen? How could you simulate the situation to generate experimental data about the likelihood of each result?

Each plan for simulating the situation must account for the following:

- a miss

- a hit followed by a miss

- a hit followed by a hit

This discussion should raise the question of how a simulation will handle the fact that this is a dependent relationship. Remind students that when they analyzed the Deep in the Dungeon game, they simulated playing the game by using number cubes, spinners, coins, or colored blocks to generate random decisions about which path to take at each fork in the maze.

Could we use any of these methods to simulate Nicky's free-throw shooting average of 60%?

Here are three of the ways students might simulate this situation:

- Spin a spinner with two sections—one with a 216° (60% of 360°) central angle for a hit, the other with a 144° (40% of 360°) central angle for a miss—that represent the probability of making or missing the shot. If the first spin lands in the hit section, the spinner is spun a second time. If the first spin lands in the miss section, the simulation is over.

- Roll a ten-sided number cube, letting 1, 2, 3, 4, 5, and 6 represent making the shot and 7, 8, 9, 10 (or 0) represent missing the shot. The number cube is rolled a second time only if the first roll lands on 1, 2, 3, 4, 5, or 6.

- Draw a colored block from a container holding ten blocks, six of one color to represent making the shot and four of another color to represent missing the shot. If the first block drawn is of the color representing making the shot, it is returned to the container and a second block is drawn.

If students choose to use a spinner for the simulation, they can make their own or use the spinners on Labsheet 5.1. (Two spinners are on each labsheet; simply cut the labsheet in half.)

To help students choose a method or methods, demonstrate how to simulate a one-and-one free-throw situation using several of the class's suggestions. Make sure students understand what data they need to record. The score from each trial is what is of interest; the data collected will be the number of times the simulation results in scores of 0 points, 1 point, and 2 points. Demonstrate trials that end with one spin (or toss or draw) and that require two spins. The number of spins in a trial depends on whether the first spin represented making the shot or missing it.

Take this opportunity to remind students about two important ideas: (1) the probability of an outcome not happening is 1 minus the probability of it happening, and (2) the probability of making or missing on the second shot is still 60%.

When Nicky goes to the line for her first shot, what is the probability that she will make the shot? *(60%)* **What is the probability that she will miss the shot?** *(40%)* **If she makes the first shot, what is the probability that she will make the second shot?**

Some students may argue that the fact that Nicky made the first shot must be accounted for by recomputing the probability. Point out that the probability has not changed: Nicky is still a 60% free-throw shooter. The basketball has no "memory" of how she did on her first shot.

Explore

Let students work in pairs to conduct the experiment with whatever simulation methods they choose and to address the remaining parts of the problem. Save the follow-up for the summary.

As you circulate, check that each pair has a reasonable simulation method and understands how to collect their data. Make sure students are not gathering data that do not accurately represent the situation; each pair's results will contribute to the experimental probability of the class's combined data set, so all should be accurate.

Ask pairs questions about what they are discovering. In particular, ask them to think about how the second shot is affected by, or how it depends on, what happens on the first shot.

Summarize

Have the class combine all their collected data and find the overall experimental probabilities.

Ask two or three pairs to explain how they found their theoretical probabilities. Following is one way to use a 10 by 10 grid to make an area model of the situation and to assign theoretical probabilities. You may want to use a transparent 10 by 10 grid to show a couple of models.

Nicky's first shot has two possible outcomes, making the shot or missing the shot. The probability of making the shot is 60%, or $\frac{60}{100}$. The probability of missing the shot is 40%, or $\frac{40}{100}$. The grid is shaded to represent these probabilities.

Nicky will make her second shot 60% of the times that she makes her first shot, or an overall total of $0.6 \times 0.6 = 0.36$, or 36% of the time. She will miss her second shot 40% of the time that she makes her first shot, or an overall total of $0.4 \times 0.6 = 0.24$, or 24% of the time.

The grid analysis helps students see that multiplying 0.60×0.60 and getting 0.36 is a numerical way to find the percent of the area allotted to receiving 2 points. It is also helpful to reiterate that we need to find 60% of 60% to represent the probability of Nicky receiving 2 points. Some students might observe that the analysis using the area model is analogous to a model for multiplying fractions:

$$P(\text{a score of } 2) = 60\% \times 60\% = 36\%$$
$$P(\text{a score of } 1) = 60\% \times 40\% = 24\%$$
$$P(\text{a score of } 0) = 40\%$$

Help students compare the class's experimental probabilities to the theoretical probabilities. In most classrooms, these will be very close as there are only three possibilities—0 points, 1 point, and 2 points—and the class data will contain many trials. However, as the probability of 0 points and 2 points are similar, the class data may not distinguish between them.

When students finish discussing the problem, give pairs a few minutes to consider the follow-up questions. The challenge is for them to determine how the area model would change if the second shot were *independent* of the first shot.

As a class, discuss how the grid should be divided to represent this situation. Make sure students see that in this area model, two sections are marked 1 point because Nicky can get 1 point in two ways: by making the first shot and missing the second, or by missing the first shot and making the second.

One way to keep track of the computations in finding expected value is to use an area model. The analysis for a 60% shooter in a two-shot free-throw situation looks as follows:

Probabilities

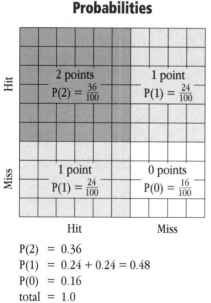

$$P(2) = 0.36$$
$$P(1) = 0.24 + 0.24 = 0.48$$
$$P(0) = 0.16$$
$$\text{total} = 1.0$$

Points Expected for 100 Shots

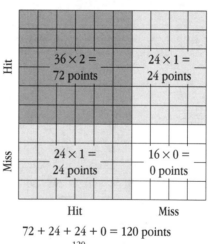

$$72 + 24 + 24 + 0 = 120 \text{ points}$$
$$\text{average} = \tfrac{120}{100} = 1.2 \text{ points/trip}$$

5.2 • Finding Expected Value

In this problem, students consider expected value, or long-term average. Reproducible sheets of 10-section, 12-section, and 16-section blank spinners are provided for use with the follow-up questions and any other problems or questions in which students want to use spinners to simulate probability situations. Supply them at your discretion after students have had an opportunity to create their own spinners.

Launch

This problem works well as a whole-class activity. Read and work through the problem with your students.

> In 100 one-and-one free-throw situations, how many times could Nicky expect to get a score of 0? *(40)* A score of 1? *(24)* A score of 2? *(36)*
>
> What is the total number of points Nicky could expect to score in 100 trips to the free-throw line?

For the 40 times that Nicky expects a score of 0 points, she would accumulate 0 points. For the 24 times that she expects a score of 1 point, she would accumulate 24 points. For the 36 times that she expects a score of 2 points, she would accumulate 72 points. This is an overall total of 0 + 24 + 72 = 96 points. Here is a useful way to organize this work:

$$0 \text{ points} \times 40 = 0$$
$$1 \text{ point} \times 24 = 24$$
$$2 \text{ points} \times 36 = 72$$
$$\text{total} = 96$$

> What would her average score per trip be? *(96 ÷ 100 = 0.96 point/trip)*

Point out that this is approximately 1 point per trip. Then, explain the following:

> In Problem 5.1, the majority of you guessed that Nicky's most likely score on a trip to the line would be 1 point—you were giving the right answer, but to the wrong question! Her *long-term average* is about 1 point, but the *most likely result* of a 60% shooter for a particular one-and-one free-throw attempt is 0 points.
>
> The average number of points per trip is called the *expected value.* We usually find the expected value over many trips, or many trials. We can think of the expected value as a long-term average.
>
> We computed the expected value for Nicky using 100 one-and-one free-throw attempts. Would it make a difference if we used 200 trials instead of 100 to compute the expected value? Why?

You may want to demonstrate that it does not make a difference:

$$0 \text{ points} \times 80 = \quad 0$$
$$1 \text{ point} \times 48 = \quad 48$$
$$2 \text{ points} \times 72 = 144$$
$$\text{total} = 192$$

Nicky's average score per trip is still $192 \div 200 = 0.96$ point/trip.

In the follow-up, students will investigate the expected value for players with other free-throw averages. If possible, display a transparency of Labsheet 5.2, and fill out the information for the 60% shooter, Nicky. Then, distribute copies of the labsheet, and have students work in pairs to analyze the probabilities and expected values for the remaining shooters.

Explore

Allow ample time for students to complete the labsheet (you may need to have students finish it individually at home). It is recommended that students work through a second example, in addition to that of the 60% shooter, before they proceed on their own.

Summarize the follow-up when all students have completed the labsheet.

Summarize

Review the labsheet as a class.

> What is the average number of points per trip that a 60% shooter can expect? *(0.96)* A 20% shooter? *(0.24)* A 40% shooter? *(0.56)* An 80% shooter? *(1.44)* How did you find your answers?

Ask the class what patterns they see in the table. Here are some patterns students have noticed:

- The probability of 0 points decreases as the shooter's average increases.

- The probability of 1 point increases and then decreases as the shooter's average increases.

- The probability of 2 points increases as the shooter's average increases.

- The probability of 2 points is always a square number.

- The expected value increases as the shooter's average increases.

> What score is a 50% shooter most likely to receive? *(Half of the time, a 50% shooter will miss. A 50% shooter's most likely score is 0 points.)*

> What can you tell about a 50% shooter's expected value from the information in your table? *(Since a 40% shooter has an expected value of 0.56 point per trip and a 60% shooter has an expected value of 0.96 point per trip, a 50% shooter's expected value will be between 0.56 and 0.96 of a point per trip.)*

> Compute the expected value for a 50% shooter, and tell me how you did it. Does your answer fit the table?

The analysis using 10 by 10 grids is quite efficient. However, some students may have begun to multiply probabilities to analyze such situations.

> What is the free-throw average for a player whose expected value is exactly 1?

From the graph made in follow-up question 3, it is approximately 62%. However, the change is not linear. You may want to have students connect the points with a slightly curved line.

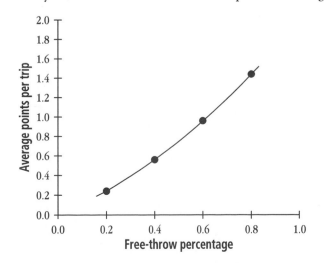

For the Teacher: A Surprising Connection

The question of what the shooting average is for a player with an expected value of exactly 1 point per trip turns out to have a surprising answer. The following is a mathematical analysis that shows how problems such as this one may be revisited in high school when students are ready to solve quadratic equations.

Let p represent the probability that a player will make the free throw. Then, $(1 - p)$ represents the probability that the player will miss the free throw. Thus, the probability of

- making 0 points is $(1 - p)$
- making 1 point is $p(1 - p)$
- making 2 points is $p \times p$, or p^2

The expected value is thus:

$$P(2 \text{ points}) \times 2 + P(1 \text{ point}) \times 1 + P(0 \text{ points}) \times 0$$

Symbolically,

$$p^2 \times 2 + p(1 - p) \times 1 + (1 - p) \times 0$$

Setting the expected value equal to 1, we can solve for p:

$$p^2 \times 2 + p(1 - p) \times 1 + (1 - p) \times 0 = 1$$
$$2p^2 + p - p^2 + 0 = 1$$
$$p^2 + p = 1$$

Using the quadratic formula to solve the resulting quadratic equation, $p^2 + p - 1 = 0$, yields:

$$p = \frac{-1 + \sqrt{1 + 4}}{2} = \frac{-1 + \sqrt{5}}{2}$$

This is the golden ratio, which is approximately 0.6180339887. The golden ratio is the proportion of length to width of a rectangle that many people consider to be the most beautiful rectangle. Many ancient Greek buildings were built with facades that incorporate this ratio.

Additional Answers

Answers to Problem 5.1

E. Possible area model:

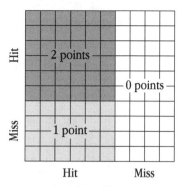

P(0 points) = $\frac{40}{100}$ = 40%, P(1 point) = $\frac{24}{100}$ = 24%, P(2 points) = $\frac{36}{100}$ = 36%

F. Answers will vary. The experimental probabilities in part D are close to the theoretical probabilities. The experiment had slightly more 2s and 1s than expected and slightly fewer 0s. As the number of trials was small, this is not surprising.

Answers to Problem 5.1 Follow-Up

1. From the area model shown below, the theoretical probabilities are P(0 points) = 16%, P(1 point) = 48%, and P(2 points) = 36%.

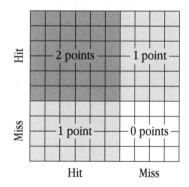

Answers to Problem 5.2 Follow-Up

1. The completed table is shown below. See the Summarize section for some patterns students may notice.

Shooter's average	P(0 points)	P(1 point)	P(2 points)	Average points per trip
20%	80%	16%	4%	0.24 point/trip
40%	60%	24%	16%	0.56 point/trip
60%	40%	24%	36%	0.96 point/trip
80%	20%	16%	64%	1.44 points/trip

2. The most likely outcome for 20%, 40%, and 60% shooters is 0 points; for an 80% shooter, it is 2 points. (Note: A score other than 0 points being most likely doesn't occur until 80%. An interesting question is, Exactly where does the most likely outcome change from 0 points to 2 points? This is the same question as, Where is the expected value equal to exactly 1 point per trip? It is the golden ratio. By guessing and checking, students can discover that when the probabilities of 0 points and 2 points are about equal, the shooter's average is about 62%. This topic would make a good library-search project.)

3. a.

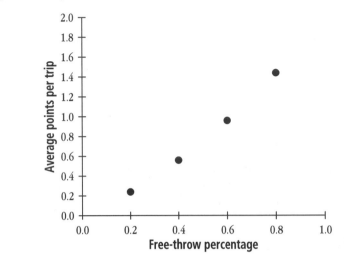

   b. The expected value increases as the shooter's average increases.

   c. His shooting percentage is probably a little more than 60%.

   d. A 70% shooter has an expected value of 1.2 points per trip. Possible area model:

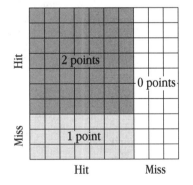

Probabilities	Points Expected
$P(2) = 0.49$	$49 \times 2 = 98$
$P(1) = 0.21$	$21 \times 1 = 21$
$P(0) = 0.30$	$30 \times 0 = 0$
	total $= 119$

average $= \frac{119}{100} = 1.19$ points/trip

ACE Answers

Connections

8a. As shown in the area model below, the probability that it would rain on both days is 9%. (Note: After working with many problems such as this, students may begin to multiply probabilities. The probability that it would rain on both days is $\frac{3}{10} \times \frac{3}{10} = \frac{9}{100}$, or 9%.)

10a. As shown in the area model below, there is a 4% chance that both tests will say Scout is not pregnant.

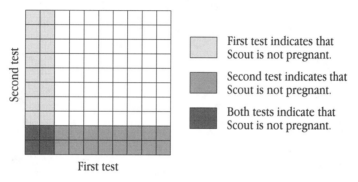

Mathematical Reflections

2. The expected value is what you could expect to happen in the long run. To find expected value, you need to know the number of times something can be expected to happen out of 100 (or the percentage) and the points awarded when it happens. In 100 trips, the 70% shooter could expect to score 0 points 30 times, 1 point 21 times, and 2 points 49 times, for a total of 21 + 2(49) = 119 points. This would give him an average of 119 ÷ 100 = 1.19 points per trip. His expected value is 1.19, since this is the number of points he could expect to earn on average per trip to the line over the long run.

Carnival Games

Each problem in this investigation involves the careful analysis of two games. Students apply and extend strategies and ideas from earlier investigations, and they continue to develop techniques for conducting simulations, analyzing situations to find all possible outcomes, and finding expected value to determine the profitability of a game.

In Problem 6.1, Drawing Marbles, students explore drawing a second marble from a container with and without replacing the marble selected on the first draw, which raises the issue of whether the probability from the second draw *depends* on the results of the first draw. When drawing with replacement, the two draws are independent: the results of the first draw do not affect the probabilities for the second. However, if the first marble drawn is not replaced, the probabilities for the second draw *are* affected: they depend on what happened in the first draw because the contents of the container have changed. In Problem 6.2, Choosing the Best Game, students find the probabilities and payoffs associated with two new games. The first game, which is similar to the Treasure Hunt game of Investigation 3, builds on the area model for analyzing the probability in situations involving two successive outcomes. The second game involves tossing a coin four times. Problem 6.3, Taking a Computer Safari, involves two games that are similar to Problem 4.1. The new factor in this problem is that students are asked to find the long-term average, or expected payoff, of each game.

Mathematical and Problem-Solving Goals

- *To find probabilities in situations that involve drawing with and without replacement*

- *To find and compare theoretical and experimental probabilities*

- *To use probability to compute expected value*

- *To use probability analysis to help make decisions*

Materials		
Problem	**For students**	**For the teacher**
All	Graphing calculators	Transparencies 6.1 to 6.3 (optional)
6.1	Colored blocks or other manipulatives (4 of one color and 1 of another per pair), opaque containers large enough for a student's hand (1 per pair)	
6.2	Coins (1 per group of 2 or 3 students), grid paper (optional; provided as a blackline master)	

Student Pages 59–68   Teaching the Investigation 68a–68m

INVESTIGATION  6

Carnival Games

Next month, Martin Luther King School is having a carnival to raise money for new computer equipment. The students are planning to have a talent show, food stands, and games.

 6.1 Drawing Marbles

A committee has been assigned to design and evaluate games for the carnival. The committee will test the games and decide which ones will help the school raise the most money. Julie and Li Fong have designed games that are quite similar.

Julie's idea
A bucket contains four blue marbles and one orange marble. Without looking, a player draws one marble from the bucket, replaces it, and then draws a second marble. If the marble is orange on either draw, the player wins.

Li Fong's idea
A bucket contains four blue marbles and one orange marble. Without looking, a player draws two marbles, one at a time, from the bucket. The player does not replace the first marble before drawing a second marble. If either marble is orange, the player wins.

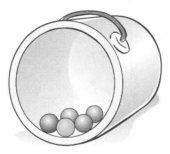

Drawing Marbles

At a Glance

Grouping:
Pairs

Launch

■ Tell the story of the carnival, and demonstrate each game.

■ Verify that students understand that whether the first marble is replaced before the second is drawn is the difference between the two games.

Explore

■ Put a chart on the board for pairs to record their data.

■ Ask questions about how pairs are collecting their data.

Summarize

■ Ask pairs how their own data compares with the class data.

■ Have the class compute the theoretical probability of winning each game and then compare the theoretical and experimental probabilities.

■ Pose another problem to assess students' understanding. *(optional)*

Assignment Choices

ACE questions 1–3 and unassigned choices from earlier problems

Choosing the Best Game

Launch

- Introduce Fergus's and Judi's games, and discuss how the theoretical probability of winning each might be found.

Explore

- If groups need help analyzing either game, suggest that they look at another group's work.

- Have students do the follow-up if they found the probabilities easily; otherwise, wait until after the summary.

Summarize

- Have groups share their strategies for finding the theoretical probability of winning each game.

- If no one shares an area model for Fergus's game, or a counting tree for Judi's game, offer these analyses.

- Talk about the follow-up.

Assignment Choices

ACE questions 4–7 and unassigned choices from earlier problems (students may need angle rulers for 4 and 5)

Problem 6.1

A. Play each game 20 times. Record your results on the board so everyone has access to the class data.

B. Based on the class data, if 100 people play Julie's game, how many people would you expect to win?

C. If 100 people play Li Fong's game, how many people would you expect to win?

■ Problem 6.1 Follow-Up

The carnival committee has decided to charge players four 50¢ tickets to play the game. Prizes awarded to the winners will cost the school $5 each.

1. If 100 people play Julie's game, how much money will the school collect? How much money can they expect to pay out in prizes?

2. If 100 people play Li Fong's game, how much money will the school collect? How much money can they expect to pay out in prizes?

3. The committee has decided that it needs only one of the games for the carnival. Which game do you think the carnival committee should use? Explain your choice.

6.2 Choosing the Best Game

Fergus and Judi think they have some interesting ideas for carnival games.

Fergus's idea

Fergus's game is played on a computer. When a player presses the *shift* key, the computer randomly throws two darts, one at a time, at the board shown below. If both darts hit a bonus space, the player wins.

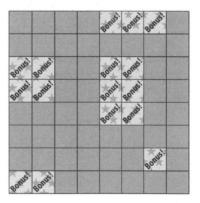

Answers to Problem 6.1

See page 68i.

Answers to Problem 6.1 Follow-Up

1. *Experimental* (based on the data in part B): The school would collect 100 × $2 = $200 and could expect to pay out 32 × $5 = $160. *Theoretical:* The school would collect $200 and could expect to pay out 36 × $5 = $180.

2. *Experimental* (based on the data in part C): The school would collect 100 × $2 = $200 and could expect to pay out 38 × $5 = $190. *Theoretical:* The school would collect $200 and could expect to pay out 40 × $5 = $200.

3. The carnival committee should use Julie's game because it has the lower expected payout.

Judi's idea

A player tosses a coin four times. If the player gets three or four heads, he or she wins.

Problem 6.2

A. What is the theoretical probability of winning Fergus's game? Explain how you got your answer.

B. What is the theoretical probability of winning Judi's game? Explain how you got your answer.

■ **Problem 6.2 Follow-Up**

1. The carnival committee decides that Fergus's and Judi's games should cost two 50¢ tickets to play, but they are having a hard time deciding how much to spend on prizes. They want to award the same prize for each game. They want to make a profit, but they want the prize to be enticing. How much money do you think the school should spend for each prize? Explain your reasoning.

2. The committee decides it needs only one of the two games for the carnival. Which game do you think the committee should choose? Explain your reasoning.

3. Jovan suggests a slightly different version of Judi's game. As in Judi's game, a player pays two 50¢ tickets and tosses a coin four times. If the coin lands heads up all four times, the player wins a prize worth $5. If the coin lands heads up exactly three times, the player wins a prize worth $2. How much could the school expect to make if 100 students play Jovan's game?

6.3 Taking a Computer Safari

Scott and Regina designed two versions of a computer game called Safari Outrun for the school carnival. The hero of the game, Illinois Bones, drives on jungle roads. At each intersection, the computer randomly selects the path Illinois will travel. At the end of the journey, Illinois will be in city A or city B.

For each version of the game, Scott and Regina have developed a set of jungle roads and a set of prices and prizes.

■■■■■■■■■
At a Glance

Grouping:
Small Groups

Launch

■ Introduce the two versions of the Safari Outrun game.

■ Read through the problem with the class.

■ Have groups of two or three analyze the games.

Explore

■ As you circulate, ask questions about how groups are analyzing the games and how to interpret their area models.

Summarize

■ Have students share their strategies for analyzing each version of the game.

■ Talk about the follow-up question.

Answers to Problem 6.2

A. P(winning Fergus's game) = $\frac{1}{16}$ = 0.0625; Possible explanation: I made a square area model and used shading to represent the chance of both darts landing in a bonus space.

B. P(winning Judi's game) = $\frac{5}{16}$ = 0.3125; Possible explanation: I made a counting tree to find all the possible outcomes.

Answers to Problem 6.2 Follow-Up

See page 68i.

Assignment Choices

ACE questions 8–10 and unassigned choices from earlier problems

Assessment

It is appropriate to use Quiz B after this problem.

Version 1

A player pays six 50¢ tickets to play the game. When the player presses the *shift* key, Illinois's journey begins. If Illinois ends in city A, the player receives a prize worth $2. If Illinois ends in city B, the player receives a prize worth $5.

Map for Version 1

Version 2

A player pays ten 50¢ tickets to play the game. When the player presses the *shift* key, Illinois's journey begins. If Illinois ends in city A, the player does not receive a prize. If Illinois ends in city B, the player receives a prize worth $10.

Map for Version 2

Answers to Problem 6.3

A. *Version 1:* The school would take in 100 × $3 = $300. *Version 2:* The school would take in 100 × $5 = $500.

B. See page 68j.

C. *Version 1:* $383 ÷ 100 = $3.83 per game; *Version 2:* $500 ÷ 100 = $5.00 per game

D. *Version 1:* In 100 games, the school could expect to lose $383 – $300 = $83. *Version 2:* In 100 games, the school collects $500 and has an expected payout of $500, so the school will break even.

Problem 6.3

The carnival committee is trying to decide which version of the game to use for the carnival. For each version, answer parts A–D.

A. How much money will the school take in if the game is played 100 times?

B. How much money can the school expect to pay out in prizes if the game is played 100 times?

C. What is the average amount the school will pay out each time the game is played?

D. If the game is played 100 times, will the school make money or lose money?

▓ Problem 6.3 Follow-Up

Which version of the game do you think the committee should select for the carnival? Explain your answer.

Answer to Problem 6.3 Follow-Up

The committee should select version 2. The school cannot expect version 2 to make money, but it could expect to lose money with version 1. The best course of action would be to alter the price to play or the payoffs to make the game more profitable.

Answers

Applications

1. Of the 36 possible outcomes when a player rolls two number cubes, 6 are matches, so the probability of winning is $\frac{1}{6}$. If a player plays 20 times, he or she will pay 20 tickets and could expect to win 20 ÷ 6 = about 3.33 times, so the player could expect to win about 16.67 tickets—an overall loss of about 3.33 tickets.

2. See page 68k.

As you work on these ACE questions, use your calculator whenever you need it.

Applications

1. In the Doubles Game, students can win carnival tickets to spend on games and food. A player pays one ticket to roll two number cubes. If the numbers match, the player wins five tickets. If a player plays this game 20 times, about how many tickets can he or she expect to win or lose? Show how you determined your answer.

2. Rashid's grandmother offers him a weekly allowance for helping her with chores around her home. She decides to make a game of it and offers him two options:

Option 1: Rashid's grandmother will give him $10 a week.

Option 2: Each week Rashid's grandmother will put four $1 bills, one $5 bill, and one $10 bill in a bag. Rashid gets to reach in and draw out two bills. This will be his allowance for the week.

The option Rashid chooses will be the method his grandmother uses to pay him for an entire year. Which plan should Rashid choose? Give mathematical reasons to support your answer.

3. Mr. Fujita hires Tasa to mow his lawn for the summer. When Tasa asks him how much he will pay her, he offers her two options:

Option 1: Mr. Fujita will pay Tasa $10 each time she mows his lawn.

Option 2: Each time Tasa mows Mr. Fujita's lawn, she will roll a pair of number cubes. If the sum on the cubes is 7, Mr. Fujita will pay her $30. If the sum is not 7, he will pay her only $3.

Which option should Tasa choose? Give mathematical reasons to support your answer.

Connections

4. a. Design a circular spinner that has six sections with the specified colors and central-angle measurements.

Section color	Central angle	Point value
yellow	20°	6
white	80°	2
black	95°	1
green	50°	4
red	35°	5
blue	80°	3

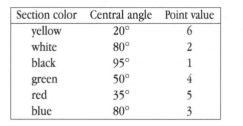

central angle

b. What is the probability that the spinner will land in each section?

c. If you spin this spinner 100 times, how many points can you expect to get per spin?

5. a. Create a circular spinner with four sections such that the probability of landing in each section is as follows:

red: 10%   yellow: 30%   blue: 45%   white: 15%

b. If you spin this spinner 500 times, how many times can you expect it to land in each section?

4a. Possible spinner:

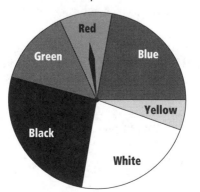

Red, Green, Blue, Black, Yellow, White

4b. The probability of landing in each section is equal to the percentage of the spinner that each section occupies.

Section	Probability
yellow	$\frac{20}{360}$ = 5.6%
white	$\frac{80}{360}$ = 22.2%
black	$\frac{95}{360}$ = 26.4%
green	$\frac{50}{360}$ = 13.9%
red	$\frac{35}{360}$ = 9.7%
blue	$\frac{80}{360}$ = 22.2%

---

3. Possible answer: The probability of rolling a sum of 7 on two number cubes is $\frac{1}{6}$, so Tasa could expect to be paid $30 about 2 times out of 12 tries. The rest of the time, she would get $3. So in 12 weeks she could expect (2 × $30) + (10 × $3) = $90. If she takes option 1, she will earn $120 for 12 weeks. The $10-per-week option is better. Another possible answer: The probability of rolling a sum of 7 on two number cubes is $\frac{1}{6}$, so Tasa could expect to earn $30 once every 6 weeks and $3 the other 5 weeks, a total of (1 × $30) + (5 × $3) = $45. The average amount Tasa could expect to collect each week is $45 ÷ 6 = $7.50. The $10-a-week plan is a better deal.

Connections

4a. See below left.

4b. See below left.

4c. If a player spins 100 times, he or she could expect to get yellow about 5.6 times, white about 22.2 times, black about 26.4 times, green about 13.9 times, red about 9.7 times, and blue about 22.2 times, for a total of 5.6(6) + 22.2(2) + 26.4(1) + 13.9(4) + 9.7(5) + 22.2(3) = about 275 points. The average number of points per spin is thus about 275 ÷ 100 = 2.75.

5. See page 68l.

6a. The probability of landing in each section is 0.1. In 100 games, the school could expect each section to come up 10 times, a total payout of $(10 \times \$300) + (10 \times \$750) + (10 \times \$200) + (10 \times \$0) + (10 \times \$400) + (10 \times \$1000) + (10 \times \$350) + (10 \times \$500) + (10 \times \$250) + (10 \times \$100) = \$38,500$. (Note: Some students may see that they get the same result by adding all the numbers on the board and multiplying by 10. If you discuss this question in class, be sure students see that the result is the same no matter how many times the game is played.)

6b. The expected payoff per spin is $\$38,500 \div 100 = \$385$.

Extensions

7a. There are 36 possible outcomes when rolling two number cubes. Each of these 36 outcomes can be matched with the 6 possible outcomes of a third number cube, which gives $36 \times 6 = 216$ possible outcomes.

7b. There are 15 ways to roll a specific double, such as double 1s: 112, 113, 114, 115, 116, 121, 131, 141, 151, 161, 211, 311, 411, 511, and 611. Or, as there are three possible positions for the single digit, and it can be one of five digits, there are $3 \times 5 = 15$ ways to roll a specific double.

7c, d. See right.

---

6. In the Funny Money game, players spin the spinner shown at right and win the indicated amount in play money. The play money can be used to purchase small prizes at the game store.

    a. If this game is played 100 times, how much play money can the school expect to pay out?

    b. What is the average payoff per spin?

Extensions

7. In the Rolling for Tickets game, players bet carnival tickets to try to win more tickets to spend on food and games. A player chooses an integer from 1 to 6 and bets as many tickets as he chooses on that number. The player then rolls three number cubes. If the player's number appears on exactly one cube, the player gets his tickets back. If the number appears on exactly two cubes, the player gets twice the number of tickets he bet. If the number appears on all three cubes, the player gets three times the number of tickets he bet.

    a. How many outcomes are there when three number cubes are rolled?

    b. How many ways are there to roll a specific double (such as two 1s or two 2s)? Do not count triples, or getting three of a kind.

    c. What is the probability that exactly two cubes will match? That three cubes will match?

    d. If a player repeatedly bets two tickets on the number 6, what will be the average payoff per roll? Explain how you found this average and what it means in this problem.

7c. As there are 15 ways to get a specific double, there are $15 \times 6 = 90$ ways that two cubes can match, a probability of $\frac{90}{216}$ = about 0.42. There are 6 ways that three cubes can match, a probability of $\frac{6}{216}$ = about 0.028.

7d. The player can roll one 6 in three ways. When the 6 is on the first number cube, there are five possibilities for each of the other two cubes, or $5 \times 5 = 25$ pairs of possibilities. Thus, there are $3 \times 25 = 75$ ways to roll exactly one 6. The player can roll two 6s in three ways. When a 6 is on the first and second number cubes, there are 5 possibilities for the third cube. Thus, there are $3 \times 5 = 15$ ways to roll two 6s. There is only one way to roll three 6s. Out of 216 rolls, the player could expect to win 6 tickets once (three times the number of tickets that were played), 4 tickets 15 times, and 2 tickets 75 times, for a total of 216 tickets. This is an average of $216 \div 216 = 1$ ticket per roll. As the player is betting 2 tickets per roll, the player can expect to lose 1 ticket per roll.

8. Della is chosen as a contestant on the Gee Whiz Everyone Wins! game show. The host gives her two red marbles, two green marbles, and two yellow marbles. He tells Della that she may put the marbles into two identical cans in any arrangement she chooses. While Della is blindfolded, the host may change the position of the cans, but he may not change the arrangement of the marbles in the cans. Della will then select a can at random and draw out a marble. If she draws a red marble, she will win a prize. How should Della arrange the marbles so she has the best chance of drawing a red marble?

9. Natasha designed a spinner game for the carnival. The spinner has 38 congruent sections, 18 orange, 18 blue, and 2 white. A player bets play money on orange or blue. If the spinner stops on the color the player has bet on, the player wins double the money bet. If the spinner lands on any other color, the player loses.

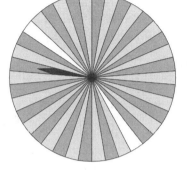

  a. What is the probability that a player will lose on one spin of the wheel?

  b. If a player bets $10 in play money on each spin, what is the average amount of money the player can expect to win or lose per spin of the wheel?

10. a. Curt has been practicing free throws. He has made 60% of his free throws during his practice sessions. The coach says that if Curt makes three free throws in a row, he can start Saturday's game. What is the probability that Curt will make three free throws in a row and start Saturday's game?

  b. Curt has a difficult time making three free throws in a row. The coach tells him to instead try making three out of four shots. What is the probability that Curt will make at least three out of four shots?

8. See page 68l.

9a. A player can bet on either blue or orange. In either case, there are 18 ways to win and 20 ways to lose, so the probability of winning on one spin is $\frac{18}{38}$, or about 0.47, and the probability of losing is 0.53.

9b. A player can expect to win $20 on 18 out of 38 spins, a total of $360. This is an expected value of $360 ÷ 38 spins = about $9.47 per spin, so the player can expect to lose about $0.53 per spin.

10a. The probability that Curt will make three shots in a row is $0.6 \times 0.6 \times 0.6 = 0.216$, or 21.6%.

10b. There are four ways Curt could make three shots and miss one. The probability that Curt will miss any one shot is 40% or 0.4, so the probability that he will miss any one specific shot and make the other three is $0.4 \times 0.6 \times 0.6 \times 0.6 = 0.0864$, or 8.64%. For all four ways he could miss one shot, this is a combined probability of $4 \times 8.64\% = 34.56\%$. Curt could also make all four shots, with a probability of $0.6 \times 0.6 \times 0.6 \times 0.6 = 0.1296$, or 12.96%. The probability, then, that he will make at least three out of four shots is 34.56% + 12.96% = 47.52%.

Possible Answers

1. To find the expected value of a particular game, you need to know the probability of each outcome. You can find these by conducting an experiment or by computing theoretical probabilities. From the probabilities, you can figure out how many times out of 100 games you could expect each outcome to occur, then compute the amount of money you could expect to pay out in 100 games. Divide this total by 100 to find the payoff per game. This is the expected value. The difference between this payoff and the amount paid to play the game gives important information about the game.

For example, suppose a game involves a spinner with four colors—blue, red, orange, and yellow, each with an equally likely chance of occurring—and a player wins $5 if the spinner lands on blue. In 100 spins, the player could expect blue about 25 times and could expect to win about $125. The expected value of each spin is thus $125 ÷ 100 = $1.25. If the player has to pay to spin— for example, $0.50—the player's average winnings per spin would be $1.25 – $0.50 = $0.75.

2. See page 68m.

Mathematical Reflections

In this investigation, you evaluated potential carnival games. You were interested in the amount of money the school could expect to pay out if the games were played many times. These questions will help you summarize what you have learned:

1 Suppose the principal wants to make sure the school won't lose money at the carnival. How would you explain to the principal how the long-term average of each game, or the expected value, can be computed? Use an example to clarify your explanation.

2 How can expected value help you make decisions in situations involving probabilities and payoffs? Use an example if it helps you to explain your thinking.

Think about your answers to these questions, discuss your ideas with other students and your teacher, and then write a summary of your findings in your journal.

Tips for the Linguistically Diverse Classroom

Original Rebus The Original Rebus technique is described in detail in *Getting to Know Connected Mathematics*. Students make a copy of the text before it is discussed. During the discussion, they generate their own rebuses for words and phrases they do not understand; the words are made comprehensible through pictures, objects, or demonstrations. Example: Question 1—Key words and phrases for which students might make rebuses are *principal* (stick figure), *school* (building with flag), *money* ($), *carnival* (carnival booth), *long-term average* (spinner labeled *100 Spins*).

TEACHING THE INVESTIGATION

6.1 • Drawing Marbles

In this problem, students analyze two games. In each game, a player draws two marbles from a container—in one game, the first marble is replaced before the second is drawn; in the other game, the first marble is not replaced before the second is drawn. Thus, the probability of drawing a particular marble in each game is different. Groups of students simulate each game, then collect and analyze the data generated by the entire class. Then, they find the expected profit from each game.

Launch

Tell the story of the school carnival, and describe Julie's and Li Fong's games.

Put four blue marbles and one orange marble (or use whatever manipulatives and colors you have available) into an opaque container, and let students get a sense of how each game is played. As the class experiments, ask questions about what they are discovering.

> In each game, how likely do you think it is that a player will draw orange on a turn (two draws): not very likely, reasonably likely, or very likely? *(Many students will think that this is not very likely or even reasonably likely.)* In this problem, you will gather evidence that will help you decide whether your guesses are reasonable.
>
> Tell me your preliminary ideas about whether you think a player is more likely to win Julie's game or Li Fong's game.
>
> What is the same about the two games? What is different?

The issue of replacement should arise, which is the essential difference between the two games.

> How many games out of 100 do you think a player could expect to win Julie's game?
>
> How many games out of 100 do you think a player could expect to win Li Fong's game?
>
> Because we don't have enough information to decide these answers for certain, we are just making guesses, or conjectures, at this time.

Arrange students in pairs to play the games and to work on the problem and follow-up.

> As you work with your partner to figure out the likelihood of winning each game, think about what effects the difference between the games has on the probability of winning each game.

Explore

Pairs will play each game 20 times. Set up a chart on the board for each pair to record their data.

Julie's Game			Li Fong's Game	
Draws orange	Doesn't draw orange		Draws orange	Doesn't draw orange

As you circulate, ask questions about what students are doing.

> How are you conducting your experiment?

Students should be beginning to understand the concepts of bias and randomness.

> Do you think you are conducting your experiment in a way that won't bias the outcome? Why?

> What are you doing to be sure you are collecting data according to the rules for each game?

> Does every marble in the container have the same chance of being selected on a particular draw?

Students should realize that mixing the marbles after each draw will help make the choices random.

Once all results are recorded, students can determine the experimental probabilities based on the class data and answer parts B and C and the follow-up questions.

Summarize

When the class is ready, ask pairs to discuss how their results for each game compare with the overall class results.

> Which do you have more confidence in, your own data or the class data? Why?

Students should realize the importance of conducting a sufficient number of trials from which to compute experimental probabilities.

There are many other questions about the class data that may be of interest to your students. Here are some examples:

> Of the data collected by each pair, what is the *range* for the number of wins (the number of orange marbles drawn) out of 20 turns for each game?

What is the *median* number of wins? What is the *mean* number of wins?

Based on their own data, which pair would predict the greatest likelihood of winning each game? Why?

Based on their data, which pair would predict the least likelihood of winning each game? Why?

Now, have the class do a theoretical analysis of each game. Ask students to work individually to list all the possible outcomes of each game and to compute the theoretical probabilities. Then, have them confer with their partners.

Bring the class back together, and look at a couple of examples of how students listed the possible outcomes for Julie's game.

Because counting trees are an important analysis method, create a counting tree with the class if no one has shared one as a way to analyze the game. Counting trees will clearly show how the two situations are different.

Counting Tree for Julie's Game

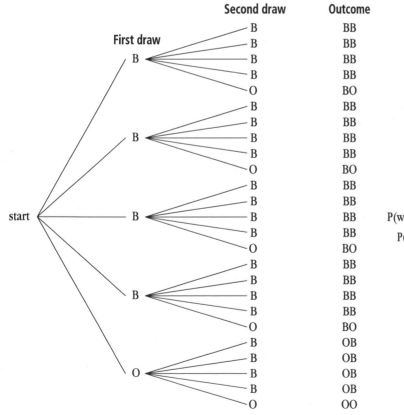

$$P(\text{winning}) = \tfrac{9}{25} = 0.36$$
$$P(\text{losing}) = \tfrac{16}{25} = 0.64$$

Students may find the analysis of Li Fong's game more challenging. Again, have them share their ideas. Be sure a counting tree is included as one analysis method.

Counting Tree for Li Fong's Game

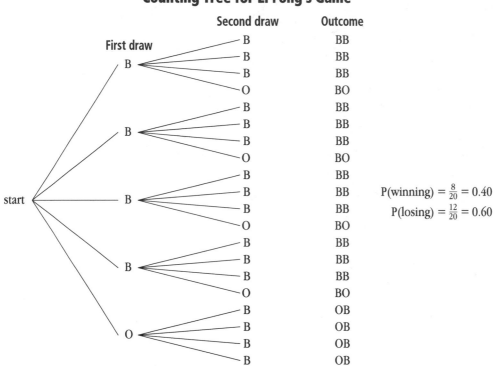

	Second draw	Outcome

First draw

$$P(\text{winning}) = \tfrac{8}{20} = 0.40$$
$$P(\text{losing}) = \tfrac{12}{20} = 0.60$$

By comparing the two counting trees, students can see how the analysis accounts for the fact that, in Li Fong's game, the bucket's contents are different on the second draw.

Next, help the class compare the experimental probabilities with the theoretical probabilities for each game. They should be reasonably close and show that a player has a greater likelihood of winning Li Fong's game than Julie's game.

Discuss the follow-up questions. You may want to have the class redo the questions using the theoretical probabilities rather than the experimental probabilities and compare the two results and what will happen in the long run.

As a quick assessment of whether the class can find a long-term average based on theoretical probabilities, you might pose the following problem:

> Two orange and three blue marbles are in a bucket. Two marbles are drawn out, one at a time, without replacement. A player pays $2 to play and wins $4 if the colors of the marbles match.
>
> If 100 people play this game, how much money could the school expect to collect? *($200)* How much money could the school expect to pay out? *(A list of all the possible outcomes will show that the probability of getting a match is $\frac{40}{100}$, which means that the school could expect to pay out $160.)*

6.2 • Choosing the Best Game

This problem also involves the analysis of two games. Fergus's game, which involves a grid similar to those used in the Treasure Hunt game in Investigation 3, builds on the area model for analyzing the probability that two successive outcomes will occur. Judi's coin-toss game foreshadows the concept of binomial probabilities, which is introduced in Investigation 7.

Launch

Copy the dartboard onto the chalkboard, or display Transparency 6.2, and explain Fergus's game. Make sure everyone understands how it is played.

> Do you think Fergus's game favors the school or the player? Why?

> How could you determine the probability of winning this game?

Students may mention conducting an experiment or making an area model. Focus the class's attention on performing a theoretical analysis by dividing a square.

> If you wanted to make an area model to find the probability of winning this game, how would you divide a square to represent the tossing of the first dart?

Some students will probably suggest using a 64-square grid, grouping the bonus spaces together, and shading the grid to divide the two sections; for example:

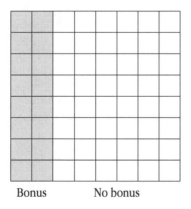

Bonus   No bonus

At this time, do not try to encourage students to describe the two areas with fractional names. Leave that for them to figure out during their exploration of the problem.

> How would you divide the square to represent the tossing of the second dart?

Again, you are asking this question to get ideas on the table, not to resolve the problem. To represent the tossing of the second dart, students must consider whether the outcome of the first dart affects the outcome of the second dart. Some students may see that if the first dart does not hit a bonus space, the player loses regardless of what happens with the second dart.

Next, describe Judi's game. You will probably need to toss a coin four times and list the outcomes so that the class understands how her game is played.

> Do you think Judi's game favors the school or the player? Why?

> How could you determine the probability of winning this game?

After the class has taken a stance on whom the game favors, have them work in groups of two or three to analyze each game, gathering evidence that will tell whether their guesses in each case are reasonable.

Explore

Some groups may need help getting started using an area model to find the probabilities in Fergus's game. Encourage them to try to figure this out for themselves. If they are still struggling, suggest they talk with and look at how another group made theirs. Other groups may need to be encouraged to think about how to create a list of the possible outcomes in Judi's game. If so, ask them how the class has done this on past problems (they have made organized lists and counting trees). Again, if they are stuck, suggest they talk to and look at how another group approached the problem.

If students are having no trouble determining the probability of winning each game, have them move on to the follow-up, in which they will determine the long-term average payout of each game.

If some groups are struggling to find the theoretical probabilities or have incorrect probabilities, postpone the follow-up until after the summary of the problem, so that students will be working with the correct probabilities.

Summarize

Have groups discuss their various strategies for finding the theoretical probability of winning each game. For Fergus's game, most students will notice that the probability of the first dart landing in a bonus space is $\frac{16}{64} = \frac{1}{4}$, or 0.25. If all the bonus spaces are grouped together, the area model might look something like these:

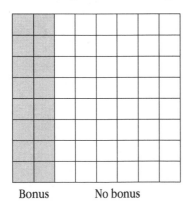

Bonus   No bonus

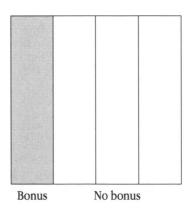

Bonus   No bonus

The second dart has the same probability of landing in a bonus space as the first dart had. So, $\frac{1}{4}$ of the $\frac{1}{4}$ successful first attempts will be matched with a second success, for an overall probability of $\frac{1}{4} \times \frac{1}{4} = \frac{1}{16}$, or 0.0625.

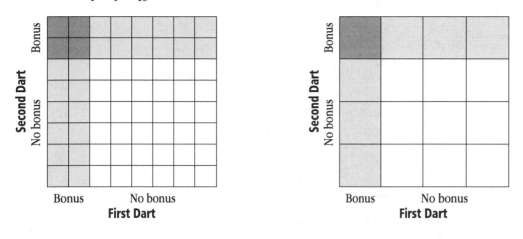

If students have not yet realized that they can multiply probabilities, focus only on the area representation. Ask whether a 10 by 10 grid could be used to represent the situation. Students need to realize that what is important in making an area model is (1) to subdivide the area so that it accurately reflects the probabilities at each stage, and (2) to add any grid lines needed to allow each section that they are interested in to be named as a fractional part of the whole square. The size of the square does not make a difference as long as the divisions are accurate and the sections of the square can be named with a fraction or a percent.

Next, talk about Judi's game. Students may have found different ways to list the possible outcomes. If no one presents a counting tree, ask whether one could be used. With the students' assistance, demonstrate how to construct a counting tree for this game.

The counting tree below shows that Judi's game has 16 equally likely outcomes. The analysis shows that the probability of winning Judi's coin game is greater than the probability of winning Fergus's computer game.

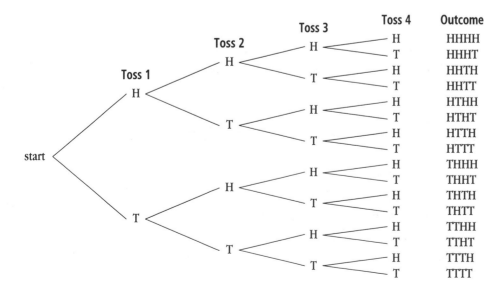

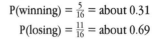

P(winning) $= \frac{5}{16} =$ about 0.31
P(losing) $= \frac{11}{16} =$ about 0.69

Ask students the following question to assess how they are making sense of the outcomes:

> Can Judi's coin game be played by tossing four coins all at once, rather than one coin four times?

This is a subtle point. If the coins are fair, there is no difference in the possible outcomes.

Move on to the follow-up questions. Groups may have very different ideas about what an appropriate payoff would be. The important thing to verify in this discussion is that each group has considered *how much* will be collected and *how much* the school could expect to pay out. A game is not useful for the carnival unless the school can expect to profit from it.

For each game, the school would collect $100 for 100 players; the payoff must be less than this amount. Make sure the class addresses the idea that if the probability of winning a game is relatively small, the payoff can be greater than it can be if the probability of winning is greater.

For each prize amount students suggest, ask for the amount collected and paid out for 100 players. This will ensure that students are basing their arguments on evidence. The difference between the two numbers—the amount collected and the amount paid out—is the expected profit.

The average amount a player could expect to win per trial of each game is the *expected value* of that game. The expected value can be found by dividing the total payoff over 100 games by 100. If the expected value is less than $1.00 (the cost to play), the school could expect to profit in the long run. If the expected value is greater than $1.00, the school could expect to lose money in the long run.

6.3 • Taking a Computer Safari

These games give students another opportunity to use area models for determining probabilities.

Launch

Talk about the two versions of the Safari Outrun game with the class, and review how each is played. Students should recognize that the plan of the Safari Outrun game is similar to that of the Deep in the Dungeon game in Problem 4.1. Read through the problem with students so they will know what is expected.

Have groups of two or three analyze each version of the game and then answer the follow-up question.

Explore

As you circulate, ask groups to explain how they are analyzing each version of the game.

> What strategy might you use to analyze the game and to find the probabilities?

If you use an area model, how would you divide the square to represent the various choices? How can you decide what part of the square represents each city?

Students' responses to these questions will let you know who understands how to construct and interpret area models for analysis and who needs additional work. If students are struggling, be sure to spend time in the summary addressing their misconceptions and helping them develop ways to create area representations.

Summarize

Have groups share their answers and strategies for analyzing each version of the game, and help them to resolve any disagreements. Then, move to the follow-up question, and let groups share their ideas about which game they would choose and why.

Additional Answers

Answers to Problem 6.1

A. Data will vary. One pair's results were as follows: Julie's game, 5 wins, 15 losses; Li Fong's game, 8 wins, 12 losses.

B. Answers will vary. One class's results were as follows: 76 wins, 164 losses. Based on these data, if 100 people play, $(76 \div 240) \times 100 =$ about 32 could be expected to win.

C. Answers will vary. One class's results were as follows: 92 wins, 148 losses. Based on these data, if 100 people play, $(92 \div 240) \times 100 =$ about 38 could be expected to win.

Answers to Problem 6.2 Follow-Up

1. Possible answer: Both games will take in $100 for 100 players. For 100 players, the school could expect $100 \times \frac{1}{16} = 6.25$ winners on Fergus's game and $100 \times \frac{5}{16} = 31.25$ winners on Judi's game. To make a profit on Judi's game, the prize could not be worth more than $100 \div 31.25 = \$3.20$. A payoff of $3 on Fergus's game, for example, would yield an expected profit of $100 - \$18.75 = \$81.25$ in 100 games; on Judi's game, it would yield an expected profit of $100 - \$93.75 = \$6.25$.

2. Possible answers: The probability of winning Judi's game is much higher, so people are more likely to want to play it because they will see more people winning. Also, it's more interactive than the computer game—people might get bored with the computer game. Or, the probability of winning Fergus's game is less, but if you offer a good prize people will take the higher risk because the prize is worth it.

3. The probability of tossing four heads is $\frac{1}{16}$; the probability of tossing three heads is $\frac{4}{16}$. In 100 games, the school would collect $100 and could expect $100 \times \frac{1}{16} = 6.25$ people to toss four heads and $100 \times \frac{4}{16} = 25$ people to toss three heads, so the school could expect to pay out $6.25 \times \$5 + 25 \times \$2 = \$81.25$. The school could thus expect a profit of $18.75 in 100 games.

Answers to Problem 6.3

B. The probability of entering each city in each version can be found by using area models, as shown below.

Version 1: The probability of entering city A is $\frac{1}{6} + \frac{2}{9} = \frac{7}{18}$, or about 39 times out of 100. The probability of entering city B is $\frac{11}{18}$, or about 61 times out of 100. For 100 games, the school could expect to pay out $39 \times \$2 + 61 \times \$5 = \$383$.

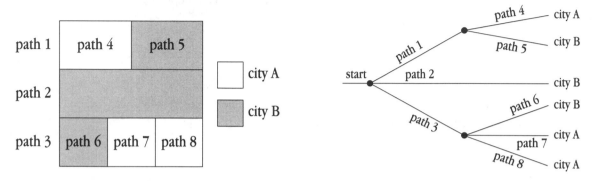

Version 2: The probability of entering city A is $\frac{3}{12} + \frac{3}{12} = \frac{6}{12}$, or 50 times out of 100. The probability of entering city B is also $\frac{6}{12}$. For 100 games, the school could expect to pay out $50 \times \$10 = \$500$.

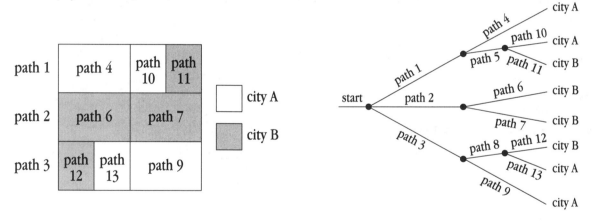

ACE Answers

Applications

2. Possible answer: Option 2 can be analyzed with a list or a counting tree.

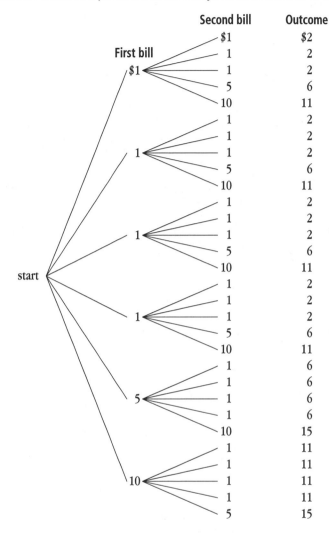

Out of 30 possible outcomes, Rashid can get $15 in 2 ways, $11 in 8 ways, $6 in 8 ways, and $2 in 12 ways. The total amount he could expect to collect in 30 weeks is (2 × $15) + (8 × $11) + (8 × $6) + (12 × $2) = $190. If he takes option 1, he will get $300 in 30 weeks. The $10-a-week plan is much better. (Students may also argue for the assurance of $10 a week.) Another possible answer (in which the order of the bills is not considered): Rashid can get $15 in 1 way, $11 in 4 ways, $6 in 4 ways, and $2 in 6 ways, a total of (1 × $15) + (4 × $11) + (4 × $6) + (6 × $2) = $95. The average amount he could expect to collect each week is $95 ÷ 15 = about $6.33. The $10-a-week plan is a much better deal.

Connections

5a. Spinners should be divided into these sections: red, 36°; yellow, 108°; blue, 162°; white, 54°. Possible spinner:

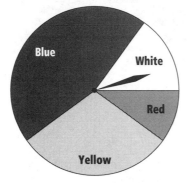

5b. *red:* $0.1 \times 500 = 50$ times, *yellow:* $0.3 \times 500 = 150$ times, *blue:* $0.45 \times 500 = 225$ times, *white:* $0.15 \times 500 = 75$ times

8. The chart shows the six basic arrangements of the six marbles—two red marbles and four nonred marbles—in the two cans. Della should put one red marble in one can and the remaining marbles in the second can. (The cans are interchangeable.)

Can 1	Can 2	Area model	P(red)
3 marbles [It doesn't matter which 3; P(red) = $\frac{1}{3}$ no matter the arrangement.]	3 marbles	can 1 can 2 / r n / r n or can 1 can 2 / r r / n n / n n	$\frac{1}{3}$
1 red, 1 nonred	1 red, 3 nonred	can 1 can 2 / r / r n / n n / n	$\frac{3}{8}$
2 nonred	2 red, 2 nonred	can 1 can 2 / n r / r / n n / n	$\frac{2}{8} = \frac{1}{4}$
2 red	4 nonred	can 1 can 2 / r n / n / r n / n	$\frac{1}{2}$
2 red, 3 nonred	1 nonred	can 1 can 2 / r / r / n n / n / n	$\frac{2}{10} = \frac{1}{5}$
1 red, 4 nonred	1 red	can 1 can 2 / n / r / n r / n / n	$\frac{6}{10} = \frac{3}{5}$

Mathematical Reflections

2. Expected value tells you what you can expect to happen in the long run. It can help you determine what the expected score of a game should be after a given number of trials. This information helps you decide whether to take a chance in a game situation. If it costs $1.00 to take a turn at a game, but the expected value of the game is only $0.50, you could expect to lose about $0.50 per game over the long run.

Analyzing Sequences of Outcomes

The two problems in this investigation are essentially the same mathematically. For both problems, students can use counting trees to analyze sequences of equally likely outcomes.

In Problem 7.1, Counting Puppies, students investigate sequences of male and female puppies in litters of puppies. In the process, they confront several common misconceptions about binomial events. For example, the birth of a male, a female, a male, and a female puppy, in that order, is just as likely as the birth of four females; but two males and two females in any order is more likely than four females. Helping students understand that the outcome FMFM is only one of several ways that two female and two male puppies can be born is an important goal of this investigation. Using a counting tree to list the possible outcomes helps students begin to see the difference, for example, between the specific outcome FMFM and the event that exactly two female puppies are in a litter of four. In Problem 7.2, Guessing Answers, students investigate randomly guessing answers on a true-false quiz.

Mathematical and Problem-Solving Goals

- **To use counting trees for finding theoretical probabilities in binomial, or 50-50, probability situations**

- **To understand the distinction between specific outcomes and events composed of a sequence of outcomes**

- **To recognize that simultaneous trials and trials conducted one at a time give the same information**

- **To use expected value to help make decisions in probability situations**

Materials		
Problem	**For students**	**For the teacher**
All	Graphing calculators	Transparencies 7.1 to 7.2B (optional)
7.2	Labsheet 7.2 (optional; 1 per group), coins (optional; 1 per group)	Transparency of Labsheet 7.2 (optional)

INVESTIGATION 7

Analyzing Sequences of Outcomes

There are many actions that have exactly two equally likely outcomes. For example, when you toss a coin you may get a head or a tail. When a baby is born, it may be a boy or a girl. In this investigation, you will explore probabilities in situations involving a sequence of actions, each with two equally likely outcomes. For example, if you toss a coin twice, you may get head/head, head/tail, tail/head, or tail/tail. If a woman has two children, she may have two boys, two girls, a girl and then a boy, or a boy and then a girl.

7.1 Counting Puppies

Scout, Mr. Maldonado's Labrador retriever, is about to have puppies. Mr. Maldonado plans to sell the puppies.

Did you know?

Labrador retrievers are the second most popular dog in the world after cocker spaniels. Labrador retrievers make especially good guide dogs for blind people because they are smart and hardworking. In fact, the guide dog who holds the record for length of service to the blind—14 years, 8 months—is Cindy-Cleo, a Labrador retriever from Tel Aviv, Israel.

Source: *The Guinness Book of Records 1994.* Ed. Peter Matthews. New York: Facts on File, 1993.

Investigation 7: Analyzing Sequences of Outcomes 69

Tips for the Linguistically Diverse Classroom

Visual Enhancement The Visual Enhancement technique is described in detail in *Getting to Know Connected Mathematics.* It involves using real objects or pictures to make information more comprehensible. Example: When discussing the information in the "Did you know?" feature, you might show pictures of a Labrador retriever, a guide dog, and a map of Israel.

7.1

Counting Puppies

At a Glance

Grouping: Individuals, then Small Groups

Launch
- Tell the story of the retriever and the four puppies.
- Get students thinking about the likelihood of various combinations of males and females.

Explore
- Have students work individually to list all the possible combinations, then gather in groups to finish the rest of the problem and follow-up.
- Help students who are having trouble start a counting tree.

Summarize
- Have students share their answers and solution strategies.
- Review the follow-up, which asks for an expected value.
- Pose another problem about the steps needed to calculate expected value. *(optional)*

Assignment Choices

ACE questions 1–3, 7, 9, 10, and unassigned choices from earlier problems

Guessing Answers

Grouping: Small Groups

Launch

■ Tell the story of the Animal Olympics quiz.

■ Have everyone take the quiz.

■ Have groups work on the problem and follow-up.

Explore

■ Give the class the answers to the quiz.

■ Have groups analyze the data in the student edition or, alternatively, have them analyze the class data.

Summarize

■ Display the translation of the quiz. (optional)

■ As a class, make a line plot of the class data, and analyze the associated experimental probabilities.

■ Compare the experimental probabilities of the class data to those of the data in the student edition.

■ Discuss the follow-up.

Assignment Choices

ACE questions 4–6, 8, 11, 12, and unassigned choices from earlier problems

---

Problem 7.1

The vet thinks Scout will have four puppies.

A. List all the possible combinations of female and male puppies Scout might have. Assume that for each puppy, a male and a female are equally likely.

B. Is Scout more likely to have four male puppies, or two male puppies and two female puppies? Explain your reasoning.

C. Is Scout more likely to have four male puppies, or a female puppy, a male puppy, a female puppy, and a male puppy, in that order? Explain your reasoning.

■ **Problem 7.1 Follow-Up**

Since female dogs can be bred to produce puppies, female puppies generally sell for more money than male puppies. Mr. Maldonado plans to sell Scout's female puppies for $250 each and her male puppies for $200 each. How much money can he expect to make for a litter of four puppies?

7.2 Guessing Answers

Have you ever forgotten to study for a quiz and had to guess at the answers? If you take a true-false test and guess on every question, what are your chances of getting every question right?

Answers to Problem 7.1

A. See page 78f.

B. The probability of four male puppies is 1 out of 16, or $\frac{1}{16}$. The probability of two male and two female puppies is 6 out of 16, or $\frac{6}{16}$. Scout is much more likely to have two male and two female puppies.

C. The probabilities of four male puppies and of the specific outcome FMFM are both $\frac{1}{16}$.

Answers to Problem 7.1 Follow-Up

Possible answer: The expected value for each puppy is the average of the two selling prices, or $225. (Notice that $225 is a probability times a payoff for every possible event, male or female: $\frac{1}{2} \times \$250 + \frac{1}{2} \times \$200$. As a male and a female are equally likely, this seems reasonable.) Four puppies would bring a total of $4 \times \$225 = \$900$. (See the Summarize section for another way to think about this.)

The following is a true-false quiz about animals. It is written in a secret code.

Animal Olympics Quiz

Tell whether each statement is true or false.

1. [secret code symbols]

2. [secret code symbols]

3. [secret code symbols]

4. [secret code symbols]

Take the Animal Olympics true-false quiz. How did you decide whether to answer true or false on each item?

Investigation 7: Analyzing Sequences of Outcomes 71

Below are the results from two classes who took the test. Everyone guessed on every question.

```
TTFT   TFTF   TTTT   FTFF   FFTF   TFTF
FFTT   TTFF   TFTT   TTTF   FFTT   FFTF
TFFT   FFTT   TFTF   FTFT   TFFF   FTFF
FFFF   FTTF   FTTT   TFFF   FFFT   FFTF
TFFF   FTTT   FTTF   FFFT   TFTF   TTTF
TFTT   FTTF   TFFF   TTFF   FFTT   TFTF
TTFF   FTFT   TFFF   FTFT   TTTF   FTTT
TTFT   FFFT   TFFT   TFFF   FTTF   TFTT
TTTF   FFFF   FFTT   FFTF   TFTF   TFFT
TTTT   FFFT   FTFF   TTTT   TFFT   FFFF
```

> ### Problem 7.2
>
> Your teacher will give you the correct answers for the quiz.
>
> **A.** Using the data above, what is the experimental probability that someone who guesses every answer will get all four answers right?
>
> **B.** What is the experimental probability that someone who guesses every answer will get exactly three answers right?
>
> **C.** What is the experimental probability that someone who guesses every answer will get exactly two answers right?
>
> **D.** What is the experimental probability that someone who guesses every answer will get exactly one answer right?
>
> **E.** What is the experimental probability that someone who guesses every answer will get no answers right?

■ Problem 7.2 Follow-Up

To figure out the theoretical probability of guessing the correct answer to zero, one, two, three, or all four questions, you need to figure out how many ways you can guess right or wrong on a four-question true-false quiz.

1. Use a counting tree to find all the combinations of right and wrong answers for a four-question true-false quiz. Use R to mean "right" and W to mean "wrong." For example, RRRR means all the answers are right, and RRRW means that the first three answers are right and the last answer is wrong.

2. How many right-wrong combinations are there on a four-question true-false quiz?

Note: The correct answers to the quiz questions are true, false, true, true, or TFTT.

Answers to Problem 7.2

A. $P(4 \text{ right}) = \frac{3}{60}$ B. $P(3 \text{ right}) = \frac{18}{60}$ C. $P(2 \text{ right}) = \frac{23}{60}$

D. $P(1 \text{ right}) = \frac{13}{60}$ E. $P(0 \text{ right}) = \frac{3}{60}$

Answers to Problem 7.2 Follow-Up

1. See page 78f.

2. There are 16 right-wrong combinations.

3. If you guess every answer to a four-question true-false quiz, are you more likely to get exactly two answers right or exactly three answers right? Explain your reasoning.

4. If you guess every answer to a four-question true-false quiz, are you more likely to get the first answer wrong and the last three answers right or to get the first two answers wrong and the last two answers right? Explain your reasoning.

5. Jim says that the probability of getting three answers right is the same as the probability of getting the first answer wrong and the last three answers right. Is he correct? Explain your reasoning.

6. When your class took the quiz, what was the average number of correct answers?

7. Will's teacher gives weekly four-question true-false quizzes. The questions on the quizzes are worth 25 points each. If Will guesses on every question of every quiz he takes, what average score can he expect on his quizzes?

8. a. How does the probability of answering four questions correctly on the quiz compare to the probability that Scout will have four female puppies?

   b. How does the probability of answering two questions correctly on the quiz compare to the probability that Scout will have two female puppies?

   c. Explain your answers to parts a and b.

3. You are more likely to get two answers right, as the probability of getting two answers right is $\frac{6}{16}$, and the probability of getting three answers right is $\frac{4}{16}$.

4. The probability for each situation is $\frac{1}{16}$, so they are equally likely.

5. Jim is incorrect. Getting the last three answers right is just one of four possible ways to guess three answers right.

6. Answers will vary. For the data given in the line plot in the Summarize section, the average number of correct answers in the class is $(3 \times 0 + 5 \times 1 + 8 \times 2 + 6 \times 3 + 2 \times 4) \div 24 = 47 \div 24 =$ about 1.96.

7. Based on the class data analyzed in question 6, Will's expected score would be about $1.96 \times 25 = 49$ points. Based on the theoretical analysis, Will could expect to average two correct questions per quiz, for an expected score of 50 points.

8. See page 78g.

Answers

Applications

1a. See below right.

1b. Ben can expect to lose 80 ÷ 80 = 1 ticket per turn.

2a. The probabilities would be the same, provided all the coins are fair.

2b. The probability of getting three tails will always be $\frac{1}{8}$; it is irrelevant what you got on the previous toss. Coins do not "remember" what happened on previous tosses.

3. Since a male and a female are equally likely outcomes for each puppy in the litter, there is still an expected value of $\frac{1}{2} \times \$250 + \frac{1}{2} \times \$200 = \$225$ for each puppy. Mr. Maldonado can expect to make 5($225) = $1125 on a litter of five puppies. (Note: Another way to analyze the problem is to make a list of the possible outcomes and look at each case.)

4a. This question could be answered by extending the counting tree that was made for four questions, though that would be tedious. With four questions on the quiz, there are 16 combinations of right and wrong answers. Adding a fifth question means adding two possibilities for each of the 16 combinations, for a total of 32 combinations. There is only one way to get all five questions correct (RRRRR), so the probability is $\frac{1}{32}$.

4b. See page 78g.

As you work on these ACE questions, use your calculator whenever you need it.

Applications

1. It costs six tickets to play the Toss-a-Coin game at the school carnival. For each turn, a player tosses a coin three times. If the coin lands heads up two or more times in a turn, the player wins ten tickets to spend on food and games.

   a. If Ben plays the game 80 times, how many tickets can he expect to win or lose?

   b. What is the average number of tickets Ben can expect to win or lose per turn?

2. a. If you toss three coins at the same time, would the probability of getting three heads be the same as or different from the probability of getting three heads when you toss one coin three times in a row? Explain your reasoning.

   b. If you toss three coins and get three tails, what is the probability you will get three tails the next time you toss the three coins? Explain your reasoning.

3. Suppose the vet thinks Scout (from Problem 7.1) will have a litter of five puppies. How much money can Mr. Maldonado expect to make from selling the puppies?

4. a. If there were five questions on the Animal Olympics quiz instead of four, what would be the probability of guessing the correct answer to all five questions? Explain your reasoning.

   b. Suppose there were ten questions on the quiz. What do you think the probability of guessing the correct answer to all ten questions would be? Explain your reasoning.

1a. As shown in the counting tree below, Ben can toss two or more heads in four ways, a $\frac{4}{8}$ probability of winning. To play, Ben would pay 80 × 6 = 480 tickets, and he could expect to win 40 × 10 = 400 tickets, an expected loss of 80 tickets.

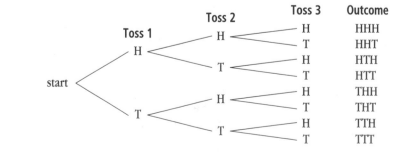

5. How is finding the probability of getting different combinations of heads and tails the same as, or different from, finding the probability of different combinations of male and female puppies in a litter or right and wrong answers on a true-false test?

Connections

6. If you studied the *How Likely Is It?* unit, you learned about the genetics involved in tongue-curling ability. Recall that every person has a combination of two tongue-curling alleles—TT, Tt, or tt—where T is the dominant tongue-curling allele, and t is the recessive non-tongue-curling allele. A person with at least one T allele will be able to curl his or her tongue.

Ken figured out that his tongue-curling alleles are tt and his wife Diane's alleles are Tt. He made this table to help him determine the possible outcomes for their children.

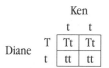

The table shows that the possible combinations are Tt, Tt, tt, and tt. This means that each of Ken and Diane's children has a 50% chance of being able to curl his or her tongue.

a. If Ken and Diane have two children, what is the probability that both of the children will be able to curl their tongues? Make a counting tree to help you answer this question.

b. If Ken and Diane have four children, what is the probability that *none* of the children will be able to curl their tongues?

c. If Ken and Diane have four children, what is the probability that only the *oldest* child will be able to curl his or her tongue?

---

5. Finding the probability of getting different combinations of heads and tails is the same as finding the probability of combinations of male and female puppies and right and wrong answers on a true-false test, since each situation involves two equally likely outcomes.

Connections

6a. See below left.

6b. See page 78g.

6c. See page 78g.

6a. As shown in the counting tree below, there are four possible outcomes, and only one is that both children can curl their tongues, with a probability of $\frac{1}{4}$.

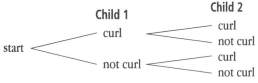

ACE

7a. See below right.

7b. Yes, Waldo might have been right. Though $\frac{1}{8}$ is a low probability, it is not impossible.

7c. As shown in the area model below, the probability of rain on both days is $0.4 \times 0.4 = 0.16$, or 16%.

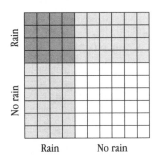

Extensions

8a. 666

8b. Possible answer: If the first number rolled is 4, 5, or 6, write it in the first blank. If it is 1, 2, or 3, write it in the last blank. Try to anticipate whether the next roll will be a greater or lesser number than the current roll and put the greatest numbers in the first and second blanks.

8c. In each blank, there is a $\frac{1}{6}$ probability of getting a 6. This means that the total probability of getting the number 666 is $\frac{1}{6} \times \frac{1}{6} \times \frac{1}{6} = \frac{1}{216}$. Students could use a counting tree or an area model to represent this.

---

7. On Thursday, Waldo, the weather reporter for Channel 6 News, said there was a 50% chance of rain on Friday, a 50% chance of rain on Saturday, and a 50% chance of rain on Sunday. The station manager is upset because it rained all three days!

a. Based on Waldo's predictions, what was the probability that it would rain all three days?

b. Do you think Waldo's predictions might have been right even though it rained all three days? Explain your reasoning.

c. If the chances of rain were actually 40% for Saturday and Sunday, what was the probability that it would rain both days? Explain your answer.

Extensions

8. Fill-in-the-Blanks is a two-person game. Each player rolls a number cube three times. After each roll, the player must write the resulting number in one of the three blanks below. The player who makes the highest three-digit number wins.

—— —— ——

a. What is the greatest possible three-digit number a player can get?

b. What strategies would you use to play the game? Explain your reasoning.

c. If the blank in which each number is written is chosen randomly, what is the probability that the greatest possible number will be obtained?

7a. As shown in the counting tree below, there are eight possible equally likely outcomes. Only one consists of rain on all three days, with a probability of $\frac{1}{8}$, or 12.5%.

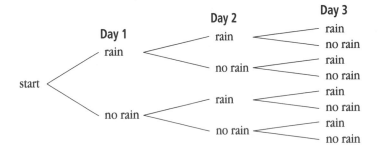

9. Brett invented a game that is played on the number line. At the start of a turn, a player places a marker on 0. The player tosses a penny and moves his marker one unit to the right if the penny lands heads up and one unit to the left if it lands tails up. The player's score for a turn is the number the marker is on after three tosses.

-4 -3 -2 -1 0 1 2 3 4

a. What scores are possible after one turn (three tosses)?

b. If Brett changes his game so that a turn consists of four tosses, what scores would be possible after one turn?

10. The largest hamster litter on record consisted of 26 babies. Suppose a hamster has 26 babies. Assume that for each baby, a female and a male are equally likely. What is the theoretical probability that all 26 babies will be male? Explain your reasoning.

11. Mindy is taking a ten-question true-false test. She forgot to study, so she is guessing at the answers.

a. What is the probability that Mindy will get all the answers correct?

b. What is the probability that Mindy will get at least nine answers correct?

12. a. If you toss six pennies, what is the probability that you will get two heads and four tails?

b. If you toss six pennies, what is the probability that you will get four heads and two tails?

Investigation 7: Analyzing Sequences of Outcomes   **77**

9a. The counting tree below shows that in three tosses, the possible scores are -3, -1, 1, and 3.

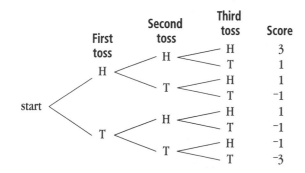

		Third	
	Second	toss	Score
First	toss		
toss	H <	H	3
H <		T	1
	T <	H	1
		T	-1
start <		H	1
	H <	T	-1
T <		H	-1
	T <	T	-3

9a. See below left.

9b. The possible scores for four tosses are -4, -2, 0, 2, and 4. (Note: Students may need to construct a counting tree to see this, or they may start to draw conclusions after experimenting with the game and checking their results after several trials.)

10. Students might have realized by now that each time they add a branch to a counting tree, they are multiplying. For example, with 4 babies, there are $2 \times 2 \times 2 \times 2 = 16$ possible outcomes. With 5 babies, there are $2 \times 2 \times 2 \times 2 \times 2 = 32$ outcomes. So, for 26 babies, there are $2 \times 2 \times 2 \times \ldots \times 2 = 2^{26} = 67,108,864$ outcomes. (Note: If students have not yet studied exponents, don't expect them to use this notation.) Having all males would be only one of these outcomes, so $P(26 \text{ males}) = \frac{1}{67,108,864}$.

11a. There is only one way out of 1024 ways for Mindy to guess the correct answer to each question ($2^{10} = 1024$). So, the probability that she will get them all correct is $\frac{1}{1024}$, or less than one in a thousand.

11b. To get at least nine answers correct, Mindy can get all ten correct, or she can get exactly one wrong. There are ten ways for her to get one answer wrong, so the probability that she will get at least nine answers correct is $\frac{1}{1024} + \frac{10}{1024} = \frac{11}{1024}$.

12. See page 78h.

1. Tossing a coin, rolling a die for an odd or an even number, spinning a spinner that is half blue and half white, drawing colored blocks or marbles from a bag that contains half of one color and half of another, and drawing red and black cards from a 52-card deck all involve two equally likely outcomes.

2. See page 78h.

3. See page 78i.

Mathematical Reflections

In this investigation, you looked at probabilities for situations involving a sequence of actions, each with two equally likely outcomes. These questions will help you summarize what you have learned:

① Describe five different situations in which there are two equally likely outcomes.

② Tossing a coin three times is an example of a situation involving a sequence of three actions, each with two equally likely outcomes.

    a. Think of another situation that involves a series of three actions, each with two equally likely outcomes. Make a counting tree to find every possible combination of outcomes.

    b. Write a question about your situations that can be answered by using your tree.

③ As you increase the number of questions on a true-false test, what happens to the total number of possible outcomes? Use a specific example, such as the difference between a three-question test and a four-question test, to show what you mean.

Think about your answers to these questions, discuss your ideas with other students and your teacher, and then write a summary of your findings in your journal.

TEACHING THE INVESTIGATION

7.1 • Counting Puppies

In this problem, students investigate a situation involving two equally likely outcomes. Scout, a Labrador retriever, will soon give birth to four puppies, each of which can be either female or male.

Launch

With the class, read the information in the "Did you know?" feature. Then, talk about Mr. Maldonado's Labrador retriever and the four puppies the veterinarian thinks she will have.

Ask questions such as the following to start students thinking about the situation (don't expect correct answers or detailed explanations at this time):

> Do you think it is more likely that a litter of four puppies will be all females or a combination of males and females?

> Which do you think is more likely: a male puppy, a female puppy, a male puppy, and a female puppy born in that order, or a litter of two males and two females born in any order?

> If we wanted to, how might we simulate litters of four puppies born randomly as male and female? What would help us to generate random combinations of puppies?

From their previous experience, students might suggest rolling number cubes (with even numbers designating female puppies and odd numbers designating male puppies, for example), spinning spinners, tossing coins, or choosing colored blocks designated to represent gender.

Explore

Have students work on listing all the possible combinations by themselves and then meet in groups of two or three to confer and to answer the questions. Remind groups to give reasons to support their answers. Assign the follow-up to be done as soon as groups are finished with the problem.

Many students will be able to find all the possibilities by using a systematic listing strategy. However, using counting trees for simple situations can help students to understand how to make a complete list without creating a counting tree. If some students are having difficulty listing the possibilities, help them to get started making a counting tree.

Summarize

Have students share their results and explain their answers.

The follow-up asks for an expected value. This is a difficult question, and students may need help. You can make the discussion more concrete by asking the class to consider several litters rather than just one. As there are 16 possible outcomes for a litter of four puppies, you may want to choose a multiple of 16 (Scout, of course, will probably not have this many litters). Help students to understand how you chose the number of litters. Emphasize that *expected value* is what will happen over a great number of trials; it is a long-term average. Following is a sequence of questions to help guide the discussion.

> Out of 16 litters of four puppies, how many litters could you expect to have zero females? *(one, as the probability of MMMM is $\frac{1}{16}$)*
>
> How many litters could you expect to have one female? *(four, as the probability of one female is $\frac{4}{16}$)*
>
> How many litters could you expect to have two females? *(six, as the probability of two females is $\frac{6}{16}$)*
>
> How many litters could you expect to have three females? *(four, as the probability of three females is $\frac{4}{16}$)*
>
> How many litters could you expect to have four females? *(one, as the probability of four females is $\frac{1}{16}$)*
>
> Now, what is the total amount of money Scout's owner could expect to collect for the females in 16 litters?

Write the computation on the board as students answer the question: $(1 \times 0 \times \$250) + (4 \times 1 \times \$250) + (6 \times 2 \times \$250) + (4 \times 3 \times \$250) + (1 \times 4 \times \$250) = \$8000$.

> What total amount of money could Scout's owner expect to collect for the males in 16 litters?

This computation is $(1 \times 4 \times \$200) + (4 \times 3 \times \$200) + (6 \times 2 \times \$200) + (4 \times 1 \times \$200) + (1 \times 0 \times \$200) = \$6400$.

> How much could Scout's owner expect to collect altogether? *(\$8000 + \$6400 = \$14,400)*
>
> So, what is the average amount Scout's owner could expect to collect per litter for 16 litters? *(\$14,400 ÷ 16 = \$900 per litter)*

As a quick check on the class's understanding of how to work through the sequence of steps involved in such problems, you might pose the question of the average amount that would be collected for litters of *three* puppies. This is a smaller set of possibilities, so it can be analyzed more quickly. With three puppies, there are only eight possible outcomes. The following table shows how to analyze eight litters of three puppies to find the long-term average.

	Sale of female puppies	Sale of male puppies
ways to have 0 females: 1	$1 \times 0 \times \$250 = \$0$	$1 \times 3 \times \$200 = \$600$
ways to have 1 female: 3	$3 \times 1 \times \$250 = \$750$	$3 \times 2 \times \$200 = \$1200$
ways to have 2 females: 3	$3 \times 2 \times \$250 = \$1500$	$3 \times 1 \times \$200 = \$600$
ways to have 3 females: 1	$1 \times 3 \times \$250 = \$750$	$1 \times 0 \times \$200 = \$0$
Total for 8 litters	$\$3000$	$\$2400$

The overall total is $\$3000 + \$2400 = \$5400$. Thus, the average amount collected per litter over the long run is $\$5400 ÷ 8 = \$675$.

7.2 • Guessing Answers

In this problem, students apply the ideas about probability analysis that they encountered in Problem 7.1. This time, the context is randomly guessing answers to questions on a true-false quiz.

Launch

Tell the story of the encoded true-false quiz. Let students talk about this amusing situation.

> If you took this quiz, how could you randomly choose whether to answer true or false to each question?

Some students may suggest tossing a coin, with heads representing true and tails false (or vice versa).

> How could you be sure you are not biasing your answers toward true or false?

Ask everyone to generate his or her own answers to the quiz. The student edition gives data for 60 quizzes taken in two classes. To get students more engaged in the problem, consider having groups analyze the class data instead. If you decide to do this, have each student list his or her answers on the board.

For the Teacher: Quiz Answers

The correct answers to the quiz questions are true, false, true, true, or TFTT.

Give students the correct answers to the quiz before they work on the problem. Have groups of three or four work on the problem and the follow-up questions. You may want to distribute Labsheet 7.2, which contains the quiz data from the two classrooms, so that students may analyze the data more easily.

Explore

In the problem, students focus on the technical work of analyzing and organizing the data. The real thinking about the mathematics comes in the follow-up questions.

The problem is structured to avoid the confusion of having two labels on a quiz question—true or false for each answer, and correct or incorrect for each grade. However, you may need to help students sort this out. The problem focuses on "grading" the quizzes; the follow-up focuses on using the graded data to answer some interesting questions.

Summarize

For fun, you might display Transparency 7.2B, which contains the following translation of the quiz.

Animal Olympics Quiz

1. The fastest-flying bird is the peregrine falcon, which can fly a maximum of 217 miles per hour when swooping downward at a 45 degree angle. *(true)*

2. The best dog "sniffers" in the world are Belgian sheepdogs named Rocky and Barco. They have helped make 969 drug seizures worth $182,000. *(false; the drugs were actually worth $182,000,000)*

3. The canine high-jump record is held by a German shepherd dog named Volse, who jumped 11 feet, 9 inches in France, in 1989. *(true)*

4. The best cat climber in the world was a four-month-old kitten who followed a group of climbers to the top of the 14,691-foot Matterhorn in the Swiss Alps. *(true)*

(Source: *Guinness Book of Records 1994.* Ed. Peter Matthews. New York: Bantam Books, 1994.)

As a class, make a line plot of the number correct on just the class data. If you did not have students list their answers on the board, have each student call out how many answers he or she got correct. Below is an example of a line plot with 24 entries.

```
                        X
                        X
                        X       X
                X       X       X
                X       X       X
        X       X       X       X
        X       X       X       X       X
        X       X       X       X       X
        ────────────────────────────────────
        0       1       2       3       4
              Number of questions correct
```

Help the class use the line plot to compute the experimental probability, based on the class data, of getting each number of questions correct. For example, in the data above, the experimental probability of getting all four questions correct is $\frac{2}{24}$.

Compare the analysis of the 60 quizzes in your math book to our analysis of our class data. Which do you feel more confident about, the small sample from our class or the larger sample from the two classes?

Once you have established the experimental probabilities for getting each possible number of correct answers, talk about the follow-up questions.

Have groups share their counting trees. Below is a counting tree of the situation.

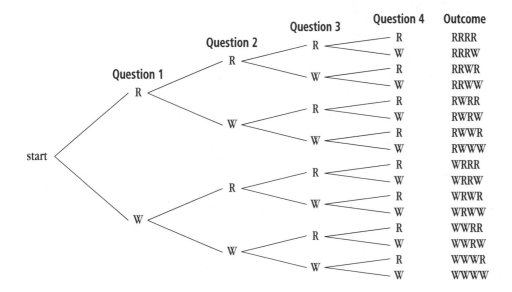

Ask groups to explain how they analyzed their list of combinations of right and wrong answers for a four-question true-false quiz.

Discuss the remaining follow-up questions. The last three questions give you a chance to review many of the ideas students have encountered about probability.

Additional Answers

Answers to Problem 7.1

A. Students might list the possibilities in a counting tree or an organized list.

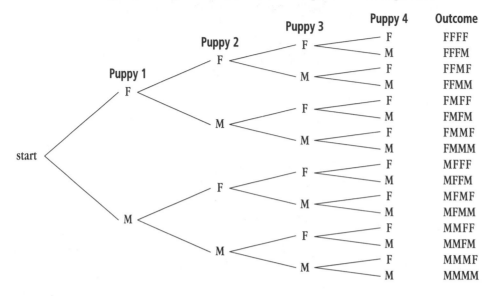

4 females	3 females	2 females	1 female	0 females
FFFF	FFFM	FFMM	FMMM	MMMM
	FFMF	FMFM	MFMM	
	FMFF	FMMF	MMFM	
	MFFF	MFFM	MMMF	
		MFMF		
		MMFF		

Answers to Problem 7.2 Follow-Up

1.

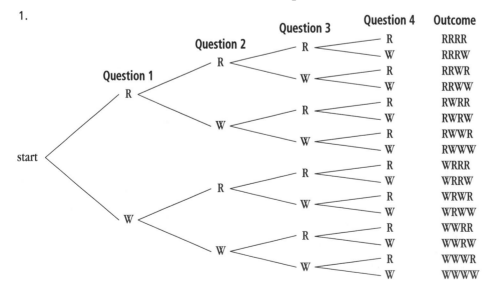

8. a. They are the same.

   b. They are the same.

   c. In both situations, two things can happen. On the quiz you can guess either true or false for each question; with the birth of a puppy you can have either a male or a female. Also, four outcomes make up each event: four questions and four puppies. This is why the probabilities are the same.

ACE Answers

Applications

4b. Students should realize that drawing the counting tree for this problem would be quite cumbersome. From part a, we know there are 32 combinations for five questions. Six questions would add two options to each of the combinations from five questions, for a total of 64 combinations. Seven questions would offer two options per combination, and so on. For ten questions, there would be $64 \times 2 \times 2 \times 2 \times 2 = 2^{10} = 1024$ combinations, so the probability is $\frac{1}{1024}$.

Connections

6b. As shown in the counting tree below, there is a 1 in 16, or $\frac{1}{16}$, probability that all four children will not be able to curl their tongues.

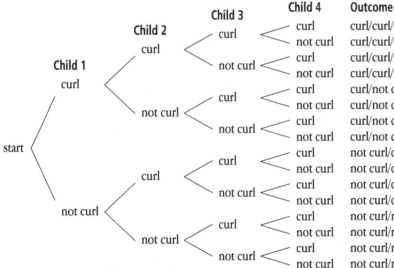

6c. As shown in the counting tree above, there is a 1 in 16, or $\frac{1}{16}$, probability that only the oldest child will be able to curl his or her tongue.

Extensions

12a. Students may realize by now that drawing counting trees is cumbersome for such problems. As discussed in ACE question 10, they might by now understand that each time they add a branch to a counting tree, they are multiplying. Tossing four pennies gives $2 \times 2 \times 2 \times 2 = 16$ possible outcomes. Tossing five pennies gives $2 \times 2 \times 2 \times 2 \times 2 = 32$ outcomes. Tossing six pennies gives $2 \times 2 \times 2 \times 2 \times 2 \times 2 = 64$ outcomes. One method of finding the possible ways to get two heads and four tails is shown below. If the first toss is a head, we can see that there are five other coins on which to toss the second head. If the first toss is a tail and the second toss is a head, there are four other coins on which to toss the second head, and so on. These various ways to toss two heads add to 15. So, the probability of tossing two heads and four tails is $\frac{15}{64}$.

Other ways to get a head

H	_	_	_	_	_	5
T	H	_	_	_	_	4
T	T	H	_	_	_	3
T	T	T	H	_	_	2
T	T	T	T	H	_	1

12b. The probability of getting four heads and two tails is the same as the probability of getting two heads and four tails, $\frac{15}{64}$.

Mathematical Reflections

2a. Suppose you choose three tulip bulbs from a box containing half pink tulips and half yellow tulips and you planted them in a line. The counting tree below shows the possible combinations of colors that might bloom.

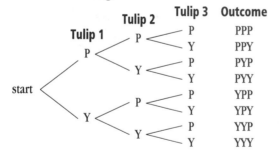

2b. What is the probability that all three tulips will be yellow?

3. Each time a question is added, the number of possible outcomes doubles: with three questions there are 8 outcomes, and with four questions there are 16 outcomes.

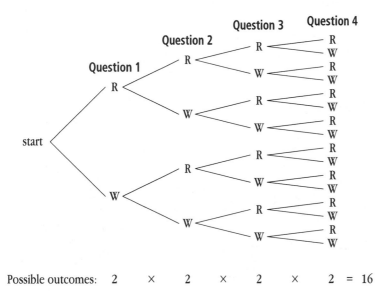

Possible outcomes: 2   ×   2   ×   2   ×   2   =   16

The Carnival Games

This project requires you to use the mathematics you have studied in several units, including this one. In this design project, you will work with a group to create a game for a school carnival and to test your game. Then, you will write a report to the carnival committee about your game.

Step 1: Design a Carnival Game

You can design a new game or redesign one of the games you analyzed in this unit. When you design your game, keep these guidelines in mind:

- The game should make a profit for the school running the carnival.
- The game should be easy to set up and use at a school carnival. It should not require expensive equipment to make or maintain.
- The game should take a relatively short time to play.
- The rules for the game should be easily understood by people your age.

Step 2: Test Your Game

After your group has drafted a game design, you need to decide whether the game you have designed is reasonable for a school carnival and will make a profit. Then, you will need to try out your game. Your group should play the game several times until you feel confident that you can predict what will happen in the long run. Keep track of your trials, and include that information in your report.

Step 3: Submit Your Game Design to the Carnival Committee

Once you are satisfied that your carnival game is reasonable, prepare to submit your game design. Your submission to the committee should include two things: a model or a scale model of the game, and a written report.

Assigning the Unit Project

The unit project offers an opportunity for students to apply the probability concepts they have studied, including expected value, in a real-world context. Students are asked to design a new game for a school carnival or to redesign one of the games that was studied in this unit.

The project works well with groups of three or four. This project may be launched near the end of the unit, sometime after Investigation 6. The project will require several hours to complete, though most of this work could be done outside of class. You may want to take half a class period to get students started. Have them form groups, review the project instructions, then brainstorm their game design. For the next few days, you might reserve the last ten minutes of class for groups to meet, report to each other, get advice from others in class or from you, and do whatever else they need to do to make progress on their projects.

A Guide to the Unit Project, which includes preparation notes and a holistic-by-category scoring rubric with guidelines for using the rubric to assess the project, can be found in the Assessment Resources section. Samples of one group's project, along with reports from two students, and a teacher's comments accompany the suggested rubric.

Create a Model or a Scale Model

With your group, prepare a model or a scale model of the game. If your group builds a scale model instead of an actual model, give the scale factor from the scale model to the actual game.

You can either construct the model out of similar material that you would use for the actual game, or you can prepare scale drawings of the game. If your group makes drawings, be sure to include enough views of your game so that anyone could look at the drawings and construct the game.

With your model, include a set of rules that explains how the game is played, how much it costs to play, how a player wins, and how much a player wins. Explain how the game would make a profit.

Write a Report

Write a report about your game to the carnival committee. Assume that the carnival committee is composed of teachers in the building (not just mathematics teachers), parents, and other students. Your report should include the following:

- *The probability of winning the game.* Give the experimental probability of winning the game that you found from playing the game several times. If possible, give the theoretical probability as well. For some games, such as tossing coins or drawing blocks from a container, finding the theoretical probability of winning is easy. For others, finding the theoretical probability may be too difficult. If you don't give the theoretical probability of winning for your game, explain why you did not.

- *The amount collected and expected payout per game.* Tell how much money the school will collect and how much they could expect to pay out if the game is played many times. Show how you determined these amounts.

- *An explanation of why your game should be chosen.* Explain why the game is worth having in the carnival and why you think people would want to play it.

Looking Back and Looking Ahead

Unit Reflections

The problems in this unit extended your knowledge of probability to several strategies for finding and interpreting *experimental* and *theoretical* probabilities. You used simulations to gather experimental data, *counting trees* and other listing techniques to find all of the possible outcomes in a problem situation, and *area models* in which probabilities are shown as parts of a whole rectangle or circle.

***

Using Your Probability Reasoning—To test your understanding and skill with probability ideas and strategies, consider the following problem situations.

1. *Sydney has a homework problem asking for designs of two dartboards that match these conditions:*

   - *The probability of landing in region A is 30%.*
   - *The probability of landing in region B is 25%.*
   - *The probability of landing in region C is 20%.*
   - *The remaining space on the dartboard is region D.*

   a. Draw a square dartboard that meets the given conditions.

   b. Draw a circular dartboard that meets the given conditions.

   c. For each dartboard, what is the probability that a dart will

   i. land in region D?

   ii. land in a region other than D?

   iii. *not* land in Region A?

Possible Answers

Using Your Probability Reasoning
1a.

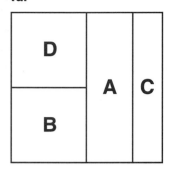

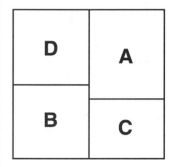

b.

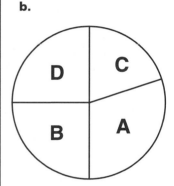

c. **i.** $\frac{1}{4}$ or 25%

    ii. $\frac{3}{4}$ or 75%

    iii. $\frac{7}{10}$ or 70%

How to Use
Looking Back and Looking Ahead: Unit Reflections

The first part of this section includes problems that allow students to demonstrate their mathematical understandings and skills. The second part gives them an opportunity to explain their reasoning. This section can be used as a review to help students stand back and reflect on the "big" ideas and connections in the unit. This section may be assigned as homework, followed up with class discussion the next day. Focus on the *Explaining Your Reasoning* section in the discussion. Encourage the students to refer to the problems to illustrate their reasoning.

2a.

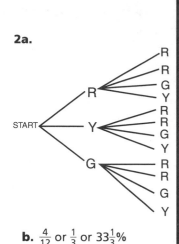

b. $\frac{4}{12}$ or $\frac{1}{3}$ or $33\frac{1}{3}$%

c. $\frac{8}{12}$ or $\frac{2}{3}$ or $66\frac{2}{3}$%

d. The game is not fair since player B has twice the number of chances to win.

It will be fair if player A receives two (2) points for each match.

3a. In 12 rounds, he can expect to win three times, thus earning 12 points. He can expect to lose nine times, thus losing 18 points. His expected point total would be –6.

b. Monte can expect to lose $\frac{1}{2}$ point per round.

c. The game is not fair since the player will end up losing more points than were won. It would be fair if the players earned 6 points for every win.

Explaining Your Reasoning
See page 80d.

---

2 *Glenda and Jim are playing the Match/No Match game. On each turn, the players spin the two spinners shown below. Player A scores 1 point if the spins match, and Player B scores 1 point if they do not match.*

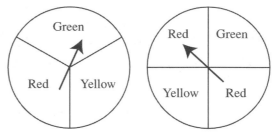

a. Use a counting tree to show all the possible outcomes for this game.

b. What is the theoretical probability of getting a match?

c. What is the theoretical probability of getting a non-match?

d. Is this a fair game? If you think the game is fair, explain why. If you think the game is not fair, explain how you could change the rules to make it fair.

3 *Kali and Tony designed a new computer game. They programmed the game so the probability that a player will win is $\frac{1}{4}$ on each turn. If the player wins, the score increases by four points. If the player loses, two points are deducted from the score.*

a. If Monte plans to play 12 rounds of the game, how many points can he expect to score?

b. How many points per round can Monte expect to win or lose?

c. Is this a fair game? If not, how would you change the points won or lost so that it would be a fair game?

Explaining Your Reasoning—When you use mathematical calculations or diagrams to solve a problem or make a decision, it is important to justify your reasoning. Answer these questions about your work.

1. What does it mean to say that the probability of some event is $\frac{1}{2}$ or $\frac{2}{3}$ or $\frac{5}{8}$?

2. How are experimental and theoretical probabilities for an event related to each other?

3. Explain and illustrate with a specific example how you could use each of these strategies to analyze probabilities.

    a. Counting trees   **b.** Area models

4. What does it mean to find the expected value of a chance activity with numerical outcomes? Give three examples of problems in this unit for which you had to compute expected value.

You will almost certainly meet this unit's ideas about probability in future study and problem solving in mathematics, science, and games of chance. These are the basis of statistical reasoning that will be developed in the *Connected Mathematics* unit *Samples and Populations* and in areas as diverse as the biology of genetics and the payoffs in state lotteries and local fund-raisers.

Explaining Your Reasoning
See page 80d.

Looking Back and Looking Ahead

Possible Answers

Explaining Your Reasoning

1. The fractions tell us that over a large number of trials the desired outcome will occur about 1 out of 2 times or 2 out of 3 times or 5 out of 8 times. More generally, we can convert these fractions to percentages and say that the event will occur about 50% or $66\frac{2}{3}$% or 62.5% of the time. These are mathematical predictions based upon the available information about a situation. The actual outcomes will be close to these predictions if the number of trials is large enough.

2. As the number of trials increases, the experimental probability approaches the theoretical probability. For a small number of trials, the experimental and theoretical probabilities for a given event are likely to differ.

3a. Counting trees offer a method to generate a comprehensive list of possible outcomes. Problem 2a shows a counting tree, as do the spinner problems and the number cube problems in the unit.

  b. Area models are useful in creating a visual representation of the likelihood of each of the possible outcomes. They show what part of the whole each possible outcome represents. Problem 1a shows an area model, as do the Treasure Hunt games in the unit.

4. The expected value or long-term average is the average payoff over many trials. To determine expected value, first determine the possible outcomes and the related theoretical probabilities. Once the theoretical probabilities are known, multiply the number of trials to be completed by each of these probabilities to determine the expected values for the given situation. For example, suppose you are playing a game with two coins in which you score 2 points if the toss is at least one head and 1 point if the toss is two tails. The theoretical probability of getting a head is $\frac{3}{4}$ (HH, TH, or HT) and of getting two tails is $\frac{1}{4}$ (TT). If you toss the two coins 36 times, then you would expect to get a head 27 times out of the 36 tosses and two tails 9 times out of 36 tosses. Therefore, the expected value is $\frac{3}{4} \times 2 + \frac{1}{4} \times 1$ which is $\frac{7}{4}$ or $1\frac{3}{4}$. You expect to score about $1\frac{3}{4}$ points per toss of the coins.

Assessment Resources

It's a good idea to have grid paper and sheets of 10 by 10 grids available for students to use during all assessment tasks.

For Quiz A, each student will need a sheet of grid paper.

For Check-Up 2, each student will need a sheet of 10 by 10 grids.

For the optional Unit Project, students will need access to commonly available mathematics materials such as calculators, rulers, compasses, number cubes, coins, spinners, blocks, and counters. In addition, students will need materials such as cardboard, construction paper, tape, and markers to construct their games.

Check-Up 1

1. Let's Make a Meal is a restaurant that lets customers design their own meals by choosing items from three categories. The Kid's Choice Make-a-Meal Deal gives children 12 and under one entree, one side dish, and a drink for $2.99.

Kid's Choice Menu		
Entrees	**Side dishes**	**Drinks**
Hamburger	French fries	Milk
Hot dog	Carrot sticks	Soda
Cheese pizza	Salad	Juice
Chicken strips		

   a. How many different Kid's Choice meals can be designed?

   b. If meals are made randomly, what is the probability that a Kid's Choice meal will include a salad?

   c. If meals are made randomly, what is the probability of a Kid's Choice meal having a hamburger, French fries, and a soda?

   d. For 50¢ more, children can also have a dessert: either a fruit cup or frozen yogurt. How many different Kid's Choice meals can be designed that include a dessert?

Check-Up 1

2. Geoffrey is baby-sitting his little sister Cela and her two friends, Sara and Katie. Cela is wearing blue, Sara is wearing red, and Katie is wearing green. Geoffrey fills a bucket with 12 red marbles, 8 blue marbles, and 4 green marbles. He tells the girls that they will play a new game. He will reach into the bucket and pull out a marble at random. The girl whose clothes match the color of the marble scores 1 point, and the first girl to reach 10 points wins.

   a. Who would you expect to win this game? Explain your answer.

   b. What is the probability of each girl scoring 1 point?

   Cela:

   Sara:

   Katie:

   c. Describe how you could change the number of points awarded for each color to make Geoffrey's game fair.

© Dale Seymour Publications®

Quiz A

1. For this problem, you will need a sheet of grid paper. On the grid paper, design a rectangular dartboard with four different-size sections labeled A, B, C, and D. Read this entire question before you start designing your dartboard.

   a. Determine the probability that a randomly thrown dart will land in each section. Write each probability as a percent.

   b. Predict how many randomly thrown darts out of 100 would land in each section.

   c. Assign a point value to each section of your dartboard to make the game reasonable. Explain your point system.

2. The game Rock-Paper-Scissors is usually played by two people following these rules:
   - On the count of three, players show a flat hand for paper, a fist for a rock, or a V sign with their fingers for scissors.
   - Paper beats rock, rock beats scissors, and scissors beats paper.
   - If both players show the same hand symbol, they replay to break the tie.

   Joey, Paula, and Cie wrote these new rules for a three-player game:
   - Joey scores 1 point if all three players show the same hand symbol, like rock-rock-rock or paper-paper-paper.
   - Paula scores 1 point if no one shows the same hand symbol.
   - Cie scores 1 point if exactly two players show the same hand symbol.

Quiz A

a. Make a list, chart, or diagram of all the possible outcomes of this three-player game.

b. What is the probability that each player will win any one round?

Joey: Paula: Cie:

c. The three friends play 200 rounds. How many rounds could each expect to win?

Joey: Paula: Cie:

d. Change the point system to make this a fair game. Explain your point system and why it is fair.

Check-Up 2

Maribeth makes 70% of her free throws when she is in a two-shot free-throw situation. Her coach notices that she gets nervous in a one-and-one free-throw situation and only makes 50% of those free throws.

1. Construct an area model for each of Maribeth's free-throw situations.

Two-shot Free-throw Situation   **One-and-One Free-throw Situation**

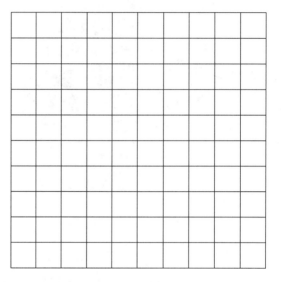

2. What is Maribeth's average points per attempt for each type of free-throw situation?

3. Maribeth was fouled 50 times this season. Of these, 20 were two-shot free-throw situations and 30 were one-and-one free-throw situations. How many points would you expect her to have scored for free throws this season?

Quiz B

Tua has created a new game called Making Green. To play the game, a player spins twice. If the player gets blue in one section and yellow in the other, the player wins, because blue and yellow together make green. The player can choose *either spinner* for each spin.

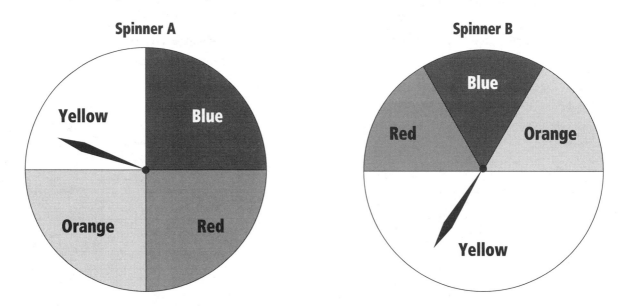

Spinner A

Spinner B

Abdul, Tua, and Darnell play the new game. Abdul spins spinner A twice. Tua spins spinner A once and spinner B once. Darnell spins spinner B twice. Who has the best chance to make green? Explain.

Assign these questions as additional homework, or use them as review, quiz, or test questions.

1. A bag contains two green marbles, four yellow marbles, six blue marbles, and eight red marbles. Draws of marbles are made randomly.

    a. What is the probability of drawing a blue marble?

    b. What is the probability of not drawing a blue marble?

    c. If you double the number of green, yellow, blue, and red marbles in the bag, what will be the probability of drawing a blue marble?

    d. How does your answer to part c compare with your answer to part a? Explain.

    e. If you add two of each color to the original bag of marbles, what will be the probability of drawing a blue marble?

    f. How does your answer to part e compare with your answer to part a? Explain.

    g. How many blue marbles would you need to add to the original bag of marbles to make the probability of drawing a blue marble $\frac{1}{2}$?

2. There are two No-Cavity Checkup prize bins at the dentist's office. One contains six hot-pink toothbrushes and four neon-yellow toothbrushes. The other contains ten packs of sugar-free gum, three grape flavor and the rest strawberry. Marquetta had no cavities this visit, so the dentist tells her to close her eyes and select a prize from each bin.

    a. What is the probability that Marquetta will select a neon-yellow toothbrush and pack of grape gum? Construct an area model to support your solution.

    b. The dental assistant refills the bins after every patient. If the next 100 patients have the same kind of checkup, how many times would you expect them to draw out the same prizes that Marquetta selected?

3. A bag contains two red marbles and two white marbles.

    a. After a marble is drawn, it is replaced before the next draw. What is the probability that a red marble will be drawn twice in a row? Explain.

    b. If a marble is drawn and is *not* replaced before the second marble is drawn, what is the probability that two red marbles will be drawn? Explain.

4. Kim spun a spinner 100 times and made a record of her results.

Outcome	Blue	Red
Number of times	86	14

   a. Which spinner below did Kim most likely use? Explain your choice.

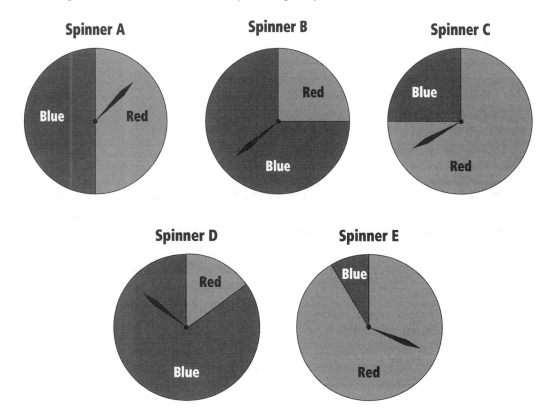

Spinner A — Blue, Red

Spinner B — Red, Blue

Spinner C — Blue, Red

Spinner D — Red, Blue

Spinner E — Blue, Red

   b. If Kim spins spinner B twice, what is the probability that she will get blue on both spins?

5. Brianna and Emmanuel are given another chance to win prizes on the Gee Whiz Everyone Wins! game show. Brianna must arrange three red marbles and three green marbles in two containers. Emmanuel will choose a container and draw out one marble. If he draws a red marble, the friends each win a prize. What arrangement of marbles in the container will give the friends the best chance of winning?

© Dale Seymour Publications®

6. Which of the counting trees indicates the possible outcomes of drawing a block from bag 1 and then a block from bag 2?

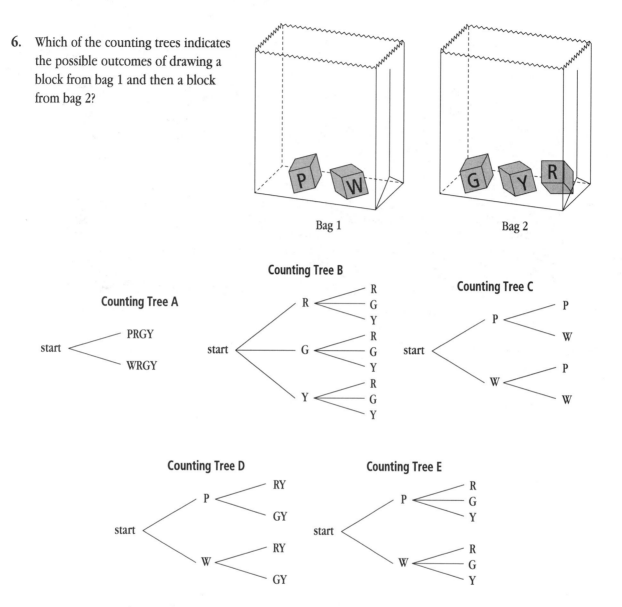

Bag 1

Bag 2

Counting Tree A

start
- PRGY
- WRGY

Counting Tree B

start
- R
  - R
  - G
  - Y
- G
  - R
  - G
  - Y
- Y
  - R
  - G
  - Y

Counting Tree C

start
- P
  - P
  - W
- W
  - P
  - W

Counting Tree D

start
- P
  - RY
  - GY
- W
  - RY
  - GY

Counting Tree E

start
- P
  - R
  - G
  - Y
- W
  - R
  - G
  - Y

7. Many states run a lottery in which a three-digit number is chosen at random each day. To win, a player must guess what three-digit number will be drawn.

   a. If each of the three digits can be 0 through 9, how many different numbers can be chosen?

   b. What is the probability of winning on any one day?

   c. If the payoff on a $1 bet is $750, what could a player expect to win over the long run?

   d. Are lotteries like this one fair games of chance? Why might a state run a game that is not fair to the players?

8. Kenisha created a new screen for the Deep in the Dungeon game.

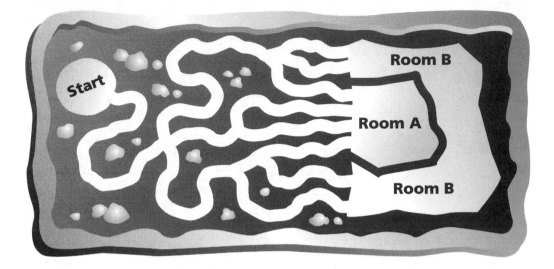

a. If Zark randomly selects a path at each fork, what is the theoretical probability that he will end in room A? In room B?

b. If you played this game 72 times, how many times could you expect Zark to end in room A? In room B?

Unit Test

1. Matt has three pairs of dark socks and six pairs of white socks in his sock drawer. Each pair is rolled together. He wants to use them to help choose his school clothes this morning. First, he will close his eyes to select a pair of socks. If the socks are dark, Matt will choose an outfit that includes the dress pants that his mother bought. If the socks are white, Matt will toss a coin. If he gets heads, he will wear jeans. If he gets tails, he will wear shorts.

   a. What is the probability that Matt will wear white socks to school?

   b. What is the probability that Matt will wear shorts to school?

   c. What is the probability that Matt will wear dress pants to school?

   d. What is the probability that Matt will wear jeans with dark socks?

   e. Is Matt equally likely to wear dress pants, shorts, and jeans today? Explain your answer.

2. Maja was analyzing a computer game similar to those you worked on in this unit. In her game, the arrangement of paths and forks leads into room A, room B, or room C. Maja made an area model to analyze the probability of Zark ending in each room.

A	A	B	B
B			
A		C	
C	A		A

   a. What is the probability of Zark ending in room A? In room B? In room C?

   b. Draw a picture of the paths and forks that could be represented by Maja's area model.

Unit Test

3. A spinner is divided into 15 equal sections, 5 red, 4 blue, 3 green, and 3 yellow.

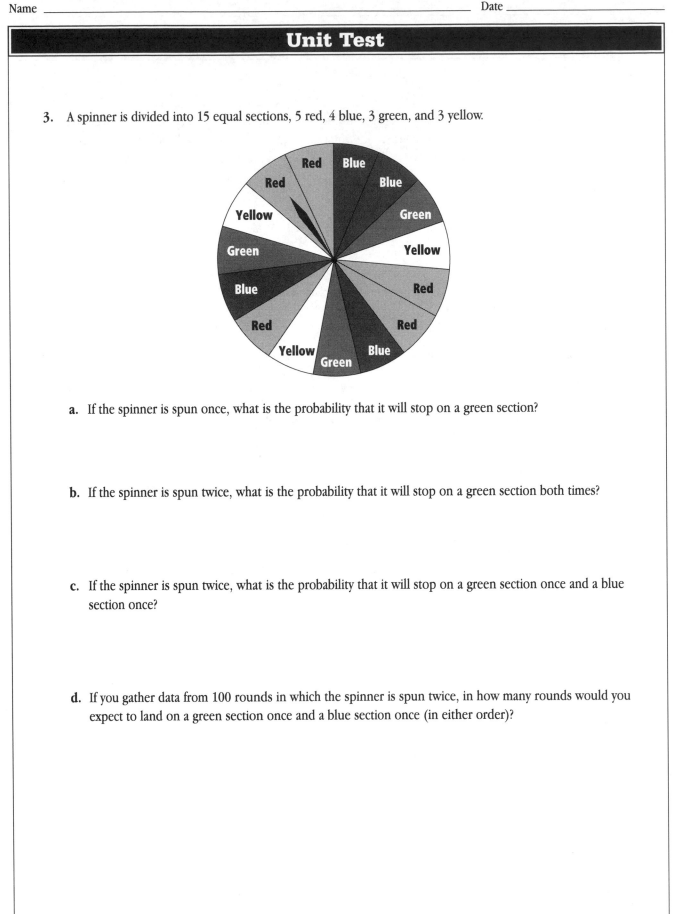

a. If the spinner is spun once, what is the probability that it will stop on a green section?

b. If the spinner is spun twice, what is the probability that it will stop on a green section both times?

c. If the spinner is spun twice, what is the probability that it will stop on a green section once and a blue section once?

d. If you gather data from 100 rounds in which the spinner is spun twice, in how many rounds would you expect to land on a green section once and a blue section once (in either order)?

Optional Unit Project: The Carnival Game

This project requires you to use the mathematics you have studied in several units, including this one. In this design project, you will work with a group to create a game for a school carnival and to test your game. Then, you will write a report to the carnival committee about your game.

Step 1: Design a Carnival Game

You can design a new game or redesign one of the games you analyzed in this unit. When you design your game, keep these guidelines in mind:

■ The game should make a profit for the school running the carnival.

■ The game should be easy to set up and use at a school carnival. It should not require expensive equipment to make or maintain.

■ The game should take a relatively short time to play.

■ The rules for the game should be easily understood by people your age.

Step 2: Test Your Game

After your group has drafted a game design, you need to decide whether the game you have designed is reasonable for a school carnival and will make a profit. Then, you will need to try out your game. Your group should play the game several times until you feel confident that you can predict what will happen in the long run. Keep track of your trials, and include that information in your report.

Step 3: Submit Your Game Design to the Carnival Committee

Once you are satisfied that your carnival game is reasonable, prepare to submit your game design. Your submission to the committee should include two things: a model or a scale model of the game, and a written report.

Create a Model or a Scale Model
With your group, prepare a model or a scale model of the game. If your group builds a scale model instead of an actual model, give the scale factor from the scale model to the actual game.

You can either construct the model out of similar material that you would use for the actual game, or you can prepare scale drawings of the game. If your group makes drawings, be sure to include enough views of your game so that anyone could look at the drawings and construct the game.

With your model, include a set of rules that explains how the game is played, how much it costs to play, how a player wins, and how much a player wins. Explain how the game would make a profit.

Write a Report

Write a report about your game to the carnival committee. Assume that the carnival committee is composed of teachers in the building (not just mathematics teachers), parents, and other students. Your report should include the following:

- *The probability of winning the game.* Give the experimental probability of winning the game that you found from playing the game several times. If possible, give the theoretical probability as well. For some games, such as tossing coins or drawing blocks from a container, finding the theoretical probability of winning is easy. For others, finding the theoretical probability may be too difficult. If you don't give the theoretical probability of winning for your game, explain why you did not.

- *The amount collected and expected payout per game.* Tell how much money the school will collect and how much they could expect to pay out if the game is played many times. Show how you determined these amounts.

- *An explanation of why your game should be chosen.* Explain why the game is worth having in the carnival and why you think people would want to play it.

Notebook Checklist

Journal Organization

_____ Problems and Mathematical Reflections are labeled and dated.

_____ Work is neat and is easy to find and follow.

Vocabulary

_____ All words are listed.   _____ All words are defined or described.

Check-Ups and Quizzes

_____ Check-Up 1   _____ Quiz A

_____ Check-Up 2   _____ Quiz B

Homework Assignments

_____ _____

_____ _____

_____ _____

_____ _____

_____ _____

_____ _____

_____ _____

_____ _____

_____ _____

_____ _____

_____ _____

_____ _____

_____ _____

_____ _____

_____ _____

Self-Assessment

Vocabulary

Of the vocabulary words I defined or described in my journal, the word _____ best demonstrates my ability to give a clear definition or description.

Of the vocabulary words I defined or described in my journal, the word _____ best demonstrates my ability to use an example to help explain or describe an idea.

Mathematical Ideas

In this unit, we learned how to find the experimental and theoretical probabilities and the long-term average, called the *expected value*, of situations with payoffs.

1. **a.** After studying the mathematics in *What Do You Expect?*, I learned the following about how to find experimental and theoretical probabilities, how to determine expected value, and what expected value means:

   b. Here are page numbers of journal entries that give evidence of what I have learned, along with descriptions of what each entry shows:

2. **a.** These are the mathematical ideas I am still struggling with:

   b. This is why I think these ideas are difficult for me:

   c. Here are page numbers of journal entries that give evidence of what I am struggling with, along with descriptions of what each entry shows:

Class Participation

I contributed to the class discussion and understanding of *What Do You Expect?* when I . . . (Give examples.)

Answer Keys

Answers to Check-Up 1

1. a. From four entrees, three side dishes, and three drinks, $4 \times 3 \times 3 = 36$ different meals can be designed. Students will probably construct a list to determine this:

burger/fries/milk	hot dog/fries/milk	pizza/fries/milk	chicken/fries/milk
burger/fries/soda	hot dog/fries/soda	pizza/fries/soda	chicken/fries/soda
burger/fries/juice	hot dog/fries/juice	pizza/fries/juice	chicken/fries/juice
burger/carrots/milk	hot dog/carrots/milk	pizza/carrots/milk	chicken/carrots/milk
burger/carrots/soda	hot dog/carrots/soda	pizza/carrots/soda	chicken/carrots/soda
burger/carrots/juice	hot dog/carrots/juice	pizza/carrots/juice	chicken/carrots/juice
burger/salad/milk	hot dog/salad/milk	pizza/salad/milk	chicken/salad/milk
burger/salad/soda	hot dog/salad/soda	pizza/salad/soda	chicken/salad/soda
burger/salad/juice	hot dog/salad/juice	pizza/salad/juice	chicken/salad/juice

b. Of the 36 possible meals, 12 have salad, a probability of $\frac{12}{36} = \frac{1}{3}$. Or, as one of the three side dishes is salad, and as every meal has a side dish, there is a $\frac{1}{3}$ probability that a lunch will have salad.

c. This is one of the 36 possible meals, and since they are chosen at random, each is equally likely, so the probability of any particular meal is $\frac{1}{36}$.

d. With a choice of two desserts, there will be twice as many combinations, for a total of 72 different meals.

2. a. The probability of Geoffrey choosing red is $\frac{12}{24} = \frac{1}{2}$, of choosing blue is $\frac{8}{24} = \frac{1}{3}$, and of choosing green is $\frac{4}{24} = \frac{1}{6}$. As red has the greatest probability, Sara, who is wearing red, could be expected to win.

b. P(Cela scoring) $= \frac{8}{24} = \frac{1}{3}$, P(Sara scoring) $= \frac{12}{24} = \frac{1}{2}$, P(Katie scoring) $= \frac{4}{24} = \frac{1}{6}$

c. Possible answer: Change the rules so that Cela scores 3 points for blue, Sara scores 2 points for red, and Katie scores 6 points for green.

Answers to Quiz A

1. Answers will need to be evaluated on an individual basis. The answers given here relate to this dartboard:

a. P(A) $= \frac{9}{36} = 25\%$, P(B) $= \frac{6}{36} =$ about 17%, P(C) $= \frac{3}{36} =$ about 8%, P(D) $= \frac{18}{36} = 50\%$

b. Of 100 darts, you could expect 25 to land in section A, 17 to land in section B, 8 to land in section C, and 50 to land in section D.

c. Assign 2 points to section A, 3 points to section B, 6 points to section C, and 1 point to section D. If you multiply the probability of landing in a section by its points, you get the same values: section A, $\frac{1}{4} \times 2 = \frac{1}{2}$; section B, $\frac{1}{6} \times 3 = \frac{1}{2}$; section C, $\frac{1}{12} \times 6 = \frac{1}{2}$; section D, $\frac{1}{2} \times 1 = \frac{1}{2}$.

2. a.

Player 1	Player 2	Player 3	Winner
rock	rock	rock	Joey
rock	rock	paper	Cie
rock	rock	scissors	Cie
rock	paper	rock	Cie
rock	paper	paper	Cie
rock	paper	scissors	Paula
rock	scissors	rock	Cie
rock	scissors	paper	Paula
rock	scissors	scissors	Cie
paper	rock	rock	Cie
paper	rock	paper	Cie
paper	rock	scissors	Paula
paper	paper	rock	Cie
paper	paper	paper	Joey

Player 1	Player 2	Player 3	Winner
paper	paper	scissors	Cie
paper	scissors	rock	Paula
paper	scissors	paper	Cie
paper	scissors	scissors	Cie
scissors	rock	rock	Cie
scissors	rock	paper	Paula
scissors	rock	scissors	Cie
scissors	paper	rock	Paula
scissors	paper	paper	Cie
scissors	paper	scissors	Cie
scissors	scissors	rock	Cie
scissors	scissors	paper	Cie
scissors	scissors	scissors	Joey

b. From the list of outcomes, P(Joey winning) = $\frac{3}{27} = \frac{1}{9}$, P(Paula winning) = $\frac{6}{27} = \frac{2}{9}$, and P(Cie winning) = $\frac{18}{27} = \frac{2}{3}$.

c. Joey could expect to win $\frac{1}{9} \times 200 =$ about 22 rounds, Paula could expect to win $\frac{2}{9} \times 200 =$ about 44 rounds, and Cie could expect to win $\frac{2}{3} \times 200 =$ about 133 rounds. (Note: Due to rounding, this adds to only 199 rounds; the sum of the individual expected values does not equal the total number of rounds. Students may want to add 1 to the expected value closest to being rounded up, which is Paula's value of about 44.44, giving her an expected value of 45.)

d. Possible answer: Give Joey 6 points when all three symbols match, Paula 3 points when all three are different, and Cie 1 point when exactly two symbols match. This is fair because if you multiply each probability of winning by the points awarded for each player, you get the same value: Joey, $\frac{1}{9} \times 6 = \frac{2}{3}$; Paula, $\frac{2}{9} \times 3 = \frac{2}{3}$; Cie, $\frac{2}{3} \times 1 = \frac{2}{3}$.

Answers to Check-Up 2

1. Possible area models:

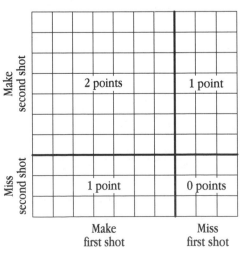

Two-shot Free-throw Situation

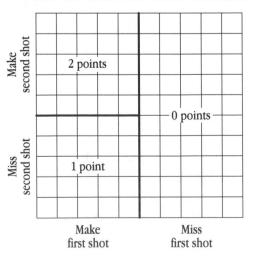

One-and-one Free-throw Situation

2. For the two-shot situation, Maribeth's average is $(49 \times 2 + 42 \times 1 + 9 \times 0) \div 100 = 1.4$ points per trip. For the one-and-one situation, her average is $(25 \times 2 + 25 \times 1 + 50 \times 0) \div 100 = 0.75$ point per trip.

3. Maribeth can be expected to have scored $20 \times 1.4 + 30 \times 0.75 = 50.5$, or about 50 or 51, points this season.

Answers to Quiz B

Abdul: There are $4 \times 4 = 16$ possible equally likely outcomes. As shown below, 2 of the 16 outcomes result in the color green, for a probability of $\frac{2}{16} = \frac{1}{8}$.

First spin	Second spin
blue	yellow
yellow	blue

Tua: In order to have equally likely outcomes, you can think of dividing the yellow section in spinner B into three equal parts: yellow 1, yellow 2, and yellow 3. This gives spinner B six equal sections, and thus there is a total of $4 \times 6 = 24$ equally likely outcomes. As shown below, 4 of the 24 outcomes result in green, for a probability of $\frac{4}{24} = \frac{1}{6}$.

Spinner A	Spinner B
yellow	blue
blue	yellow 1
blue	yellow 2
blue	yellow 3

Darnell: Dividing the yellow section in spinner B into three equal parts gives a total of $6 \times 6 = 36$ equally likely outcomes. As shown below, 6 of the 36 outcomes result in green, for a probability of $\frac{6}{36} = \frac{1}{6}$.

First spin	Second spin
yellow 1	blue
yellow 2	blue
yellow 3	blue
blue	yellow 1
blue	yellow 2
blue	yellow 3

Tua and Darnell have an equal chance of making green and a better chance of making green than Abdul has.

Answers to the Question Bank

1. a. $P(\text{blue}) = \frac{6}{20} = \frac{3}{10}$

   b. $P(\text{not blue}) = \frac{14}{20} = \frac{7}{10}$

   c. $P(\text{blue}) = \frac{12}{40} = \frac{3}{10}$

   d. The probabilities are the same. The number of blue marbles and the total number of marbles both increased by a scale factor of 2, so the ratio of blue marbles to total marbles, and therefore the probability, does not change.

   e. $P(\text{blue}) = \frac{8}{28} = \frac{2}{7}$

   f. The probability decreases slightly. Adding marbles did not keep the probabilities, or the fractions, equivalent. To be equivalent, the fraction numerators and denominators must increase at the same rate, not by the same number.

   g. You would need to add 8 blue marbles. Then, there would be 14 blue marbles and a total of 28, so $P(\text{blue}) = \frac{14}{28} = \frac{1}{2}$.

2. **a.** Marquetta has a $\frac{12}{100}$ probability of drawing a neon-yellow toothbrush and a pack of grape gum.

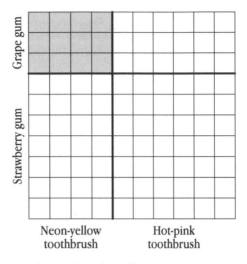

b. Of 100 patients, you could expect about 12 to draw the same prizes Marquetta chose.

3. **a.** P(two red marbles) = $\frac{1}{4}$; Of the four equally likely outcomes—red/red, red/white, white/red, and white/white—one is the drawing of two red marbles.

b. The area model below shows that the first draw has four possibilities. The possible results of the second draw in each case are listed below the corresponding first draw. Two of the 12 possible outcomes result in two red marbles being drawn, a probability of $\frac{2}{12} = \frac{1}{6}$.

First Draw

R	R	W	W
R	R	R	R
W	W	R	R
W	W	W	W

4. **a.** The ratio of blue to red in spinner D most closely resembles the ratio of blue to red in the table, so it is the most likely to have been used.

b. In the area model below, 9 of the 16 squares represent spinning blue twice, for a probability of $\frac{9}{16}$.

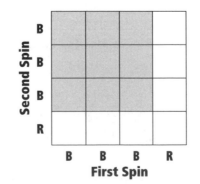

5. The best arrangement is one red marble in one container and the remaining marbles in the other container. The area model shows that the probability of drawing red with this arrangement is $\frac{1}{2} + \frac{2}{10} = \frac{7}{10}$.

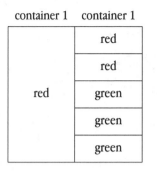

container 1   container 1

6. counting tree E

7. **a.** There are $10 \times 10 \times 10 = 1000$ different numbers that can be chosen.

   b. The probability of winning on any one day is $\frac{1}{1000}$.

   c. Over the long run, a player could expect to win $\frac{1}{1000} \times 750 = \$0.75$ on each bet, an overall loss of $\$0.25$ per bet.

   d. This is not a fair game of chance, since for every $1 bet placed, a player could expect to get back only $0.75. States run lotteries to make a profit, so they do not favor the players.

8. **a.** The square below shows the theoretical probability of Zark ending in each room. The probability of Zark ending in room A is $\frac{1}{9} + \frac{1}{6} + \frac{1}{6} + \frac{1}{12} = \frac{19}{36}$. The probability of Zark ending in room B is $\frac{1}{9} + \frac{1}{9} + \frac{1}{12} + \frac{1}{6} = \frac{17}{36}$.

B	B	A
A		A
A		B
B		

   b. In 72 games, you could expect Zark to end in room A $72 \times \frac{19}{36} = 38$ times and in room B $72 \times \frac{17}{36} = 34$ times.

Answers to the Unit Test

1. Students might draw an area model for this problem, such as the one below.

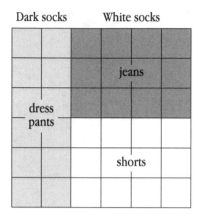

Dark socks   White socks

jeans

dress pants

shorts

   a. P(white socks) $= \frac{2}{3}$

   b. P(shorts) $= \frac{12}{36} = \frac{1}{3}$

   c. P(dress pants) $= \frac{12}{36} = \frac{1}{3}$

   d. P(jeans with dark socks) $= 0$

   e. Yes, the three are equally likely to be worn. In the area model, each region occupies the same number of squares, so each choice is equally likely.

2. **a.** P(ending in room A) $= \frac{1}{16} + \frac{1}{16} + \frac{1}{8} + \frac{1}{12} + \frac{1}{12} = \frac{5}{12}$, P(ending in room B) $= \frac{1}{16} + \frac{1}{16} + \frac{1}{4} = \frac{3}{8}$, P(ending in room C) $= \frac{1}{8} + \frac{1}{12} = \frac{5}{24}$

   b. Possible answer:

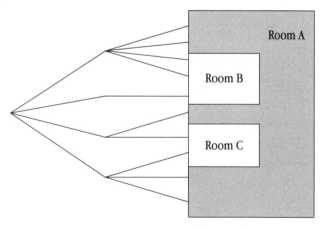

Room A

Room B

Room C

3. **a.** P(green) $= \frac{3}{15} = \frac{1}{5}$

   b. The total number of outcomes for two spins is $15 \times 15 = 225$. The number of those outcomes that will result in two greens is $3 \times 3 = 9$. Thus, P(two greens) $= \frac{9}{225} = \frac{1}{25}$.

   c. A green and a blue can be spun in two ways: by spinning green first and then blue ($3 \times 4 = 12$ ways) or by spinning blue first and then green ($4 \times 3 = 12$ ways). This is a total of 24 ways, so P(green and blue) $= \frac{24}{225} = \frac{8}{75}$.

   d. In 100 rounds, you could expect a green/blue combination $100 \times \frac{8}{75} = $ about 11 times.

The optional Unit Project offers an opportunity for students to apply the probability concepts they have studied, including expected value, in a real-world context. Students are asked to design a new game for a school carnival or to redesign one of the games that was studied in this unit. In testing their games and writing a report about them, students will need to collect, organize, and analyze data.

The blackline masters for the project appear on pages 93 and 94. This section contains preparation notes for the Carnival Game project and a holistic-by-category scoring rubric with guidelines for using the rubric to assess the project. Samples of one group's project, along with reports from two students, and a teacher's comments accompany the suggested rubric.

Preparing for the Carnival Game Project

This project works well with groups of three or four. Some teachers have groups work together to design and make models of their game and to discuss the report, and then have students write their final reports individually.

Students will need access to commonly available mathematics materials such as calculators, rulers, compasses, number cubes, coins, spinners, blocks, and counters. In addition, students will need materials such as cardboard, construction paper, tape, and markers to construct their models.

The project may be launched near the end of the unit, sometime after Investigation 6. The project will require several hours to complete, though most of this work could be done outside of class. You may want to take half a class period to get students started. Have them form groups, review the project handout, then brainstorm their game design. For the next few days, you might reserve the last ten minutes of class for groups to meet, report to each other, get advice from others in the class or from you, and do whatever else they need to do to make progress on their projects.

Some teachers have groups share their game with the class as part of their final report. Others have expanded the project into a school event in which groups set up their games in the gymnasium and students from other grades come to the Math Carnival and play the games (using tokens rather than money).

Suggested Scoring Rubric

This rubric employs a point scale for two separate areas of assessment for a total of 22 points. Use the rubric as presented here, or modify it to fit your needs and your district's requirements for evaluating and reporting students' work and understanding.

Game Design

Rules for the game (0–3 points)

3   Rules for the game are clear, complete, and address how to play the game, how to win the game, how much the game costs to play, and how much a player wins.

2   Rules for the game are clear but incomplete. One of the following is missing: how to play the game, how to win the game, how much the game costs to play, or how much a player wins.

1   Rules do not address at least two of the following: how to play the game, how to win the game, how much the game costs to play, or how much a player wins.

0   Rules are not included or cannot be followed.

Scale model or model (0–2 points)

2   Model is a neat and accurate representation of the game. If it is a scale model, the scale factor from it to the actual game is given.

1   Model is included but does not match the description given.

0   Model is not included.

Profit (0–2 points)

2   Group correctly concludes that the game would make a profit and explains why.

1   Group correctly concludes that the game would make a profit but does not explain why.

0   Group does not address profit or the game does not make a profit.

Ease of use (0–1 point)

1   The game is easy to use.

0   The game is not easy to use.

Ease of construction (0–1 point)

1   The game is easy to construct.

0   The game is not easy to construct.

Written Report

Probability of winning (0–3 points)

3   Student correctly gives the theoretical probability of winning the game and correctly finds the experimental probability from playing the game and resolves any difference between the two probabilities. *Or,* student offers an adequate explanation of why the theoretical probability for the game cannot be found and performs a substantial number (depending on the complexity of the game) of trials of the game and correctly finds the experimental probability based on these data.

2   Student has made a small error or errors and only the theoretical probability (or a reason why it cannot be found) or only the experimental probability is correct. *Or,* student offers an adequate explanation of why the theoretical probability cannot be found but the number of trials is insufficient to draw conclusions even though the experimental probability may be correct based on the limited data.

1   One of the probabilities, experimental or theoretical, is not addressed correctly.

0   Neither experimental probability nor theoretical probability is addressed correctly.

Expected payout (0–3 points)

3   Student gives the correct expected payout and enough information for the reader to understand how it was calculated.

2   Student gives the correct expected payout but does not give enough information for the reader to understand how it was calculated. *Or,* student has made a small error in calculating the expected payout but does give enough information for the reader to understand how it was calculated.

1   Student has made an error in calculating the expected payout and does not give enough information for the reader to understand how it was calculated.

0   No expected payout is given.

Data collection (0–2 points)

2   Student describes data collection, gives results, and connects this information to the probability of winning the game or the expected payout.

1   Student describes data collection and gives results but does not connect this information to the probability of winning the game or the expected payout.

0   Student does not describe data collection or give results.

Explanation for why the game should be in the carnival (0–2 points)

2   Student addresses why people will want to play the game (and says more than "they will like it" or something similar) and why it should be in the carnival.

1   Student addresses why people will want to play the game or why it should be in the carnival, but not both.

0   These ideas are not addressed.

Overall flow, organization, and presentation (0–3 points)

3 Report is clearly stated, easy to follow, and neatly presented.

2 Report is neatly presented and, with some effort, the reader can follow it.

1 Report is not neatly presented and effort is needed by the reader to follow it.

0 Report is unacceptable.

Sample Student Work

Below is a Carnival Game project presented by one group of students. In this classroom, students worked on the project in groups of four, and each member of the group wrote his or her own report. Following the project are two individual reports written by students in the group and a teacher's explanation of how the reports were scored using the suggested rubric.

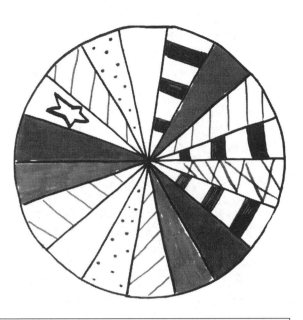

Spin-Loser-Draw

HOW TO PLAY

This game costs $0.25 to play. The operator will hold a bucket filled with colored cubes. He/she will hold it above the players head so he/she can not see. The player then chooses one colored cube from the bucket without looking. The player must remember the color of the block and make sure that the operator knows the color of the cube also. Then you will replace the colored cube back into the bucket. Then the operator will spin the spinner. If the color that the spinner lands on matches the color of the cube that you drew, then you are a winner! You will earn a prize bases on the color of the match that you got. (See prize list).

OBJECT

The object of this game is to have the spinner match the color of block that you have drawn from the bucket.

RULES

1. Must pay $0.25 to play Spin-loser-draw.
2. Pick one cube per game only.
3. Do not look at the cubes while drawing.
4. Operator must spin spinner.
5. Colors on spinner and cube must match to win

Spin-Loser-Draw Prize List

If you match two....Greens.....you get......$0.50

If you match two....Oranges..you get......$0.75

If you match two....Blues......you get......$0.75

If you match two....Yellows...you get......$1.00

If you match two....Polka-dots you get.$1.00

If you match two....Reds.......you get......$1.00

If you match two....Stars......you get......$2.00

If you match two....Plaids...you get......$2.00

Susy's Written Report

Susy

Dear Carnival Commite,

We are submiting a game for the school carnival. Our game is fun, easy, and profitable. We think our game should be in the carnival becase it will be fun for people to play. It's not very expensive to play and it could be an easy game to make money off of. We believe that a lot of people will keep playing so they can win more money, or get their money back.

Following is the probability of winning the game, first of each pattern and then all together.

Pattern	Chances of Winning	Pattern	Chances of Winning
Star	$\frac{1}{324}$	Blue	$\frac{9}{324}$
Plaid	$\frac{1}{324}$	Orange	$\frac{9}{324}$
Yellow	$\frac{4}{324}$	Polka-dot	$\frac{4}{324}$
Red	$\frac{4}{324}$	Green	$\frac{16}{324}$

Total amount of chances of winning is $\frac{48}{324}$.

We have also tested our game. Here are our results of 100 trials:

Star- 0/100   Blue- 5/100   The total
Plaid- 0/100   Red- 0/100   winning
Yellow- 0/100 Orange- 5/100 is 19/100.
Green- 3/100   Polka-dot- 2/100

Also we found how much profit we would make with our experimental data. For 100 games the total amont taking in is $25.00. We figured how much money we had to payout, depending on the number of wins for each catigory. Below is are figuring.

Pattern	Wins	$ out
Star		
Plaid		
Polka-dot	11	2.00
Blue	ﬀﬀ	3.75
Red		
Green	111	1.50
Orange	ﬀﬀ	3.75

Total taken in = $25.

Payouts = $11.

Profit = $14.

Here is the expected value theoretically. The values are out of 324.

Star   2.00   Green   2.00
Plaid   2.00   Red   2.00
Polk-dot 2.00   Blue   2.25
Yellow   2.00   Orange 2.25

$81.00 to take in
$16.50 to give out
$64.50 profit

Thank-you,

Susy

Susy's Data

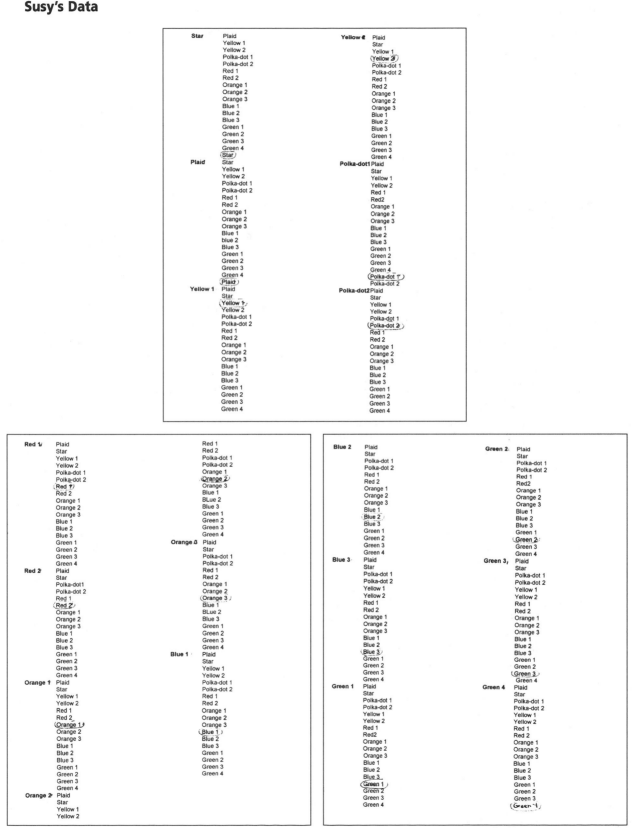

Heidi's Written Report

Heidi

Report: Carnival Game

Dear Carnival Directors;

I would like to introduce a game made for the upcoming carnival. I and three others spent time considering what the kids would enjoy playing, but will give us a profit.

Here's how you play Spin-Loser-draw. We have a bucket containing cubes. The contanents of the bucket are: 4 green cubes, 3 blue and three orange cubes, 2 red, polka-dot and yellow cubes and 1 star and plaid cube, a total of 18 cubes. For each cube there is ¹/₁₈ slot filled in matching it on the spinner. The player draws a

cube without looking from the bucket. Then the game operator spins the spiner. If the spinner matches the drawn cube, the player won! It's that simple.

Kids will want to play for that reason. It appears that it is very simple to win. Two colors, and they're in luck. And, at the low price of only a quarter, they're going to want to try their luck again and again. The prizes also appear very tempting to them.

The prizes are based on the different colors of the match. There are more greens, so there is a better chance that 2 greens will be drawn, so greens are worth less. where plaids or stars have the least,

and the lowest chance of being drawn, therefor it is worth the most in prize money.

This game has been tested. We played it 100 times. Out of those experimental trys, we won 6 times. So this game will make quite a profit. Out of 100 games, we expect to give out approximatly $11 dollars. But each game cost 25 cents, which is $25 dollars. So we will be making $14.00 profit every 100 games. We calculated all the possible conbimations of cubes and spiner. We added up how many times you could win. Our numbers came out as 48 winning combinations out of 324 total possible.

This is approximetley 5.5 wins in 100 games, which we calculated for experimetal trys.

Please include our game at your carnival. The kids will enjoy it, while you're making a profit

Thanks.

Heidi

Heidi's Data

	Bucket	Spinner	W	L
1.	ORANGE	ORANGE	*	
2.	GREEN	GREEN	*	
3.	BLUE	BLUE	*	
4.	BLUE	ORANGE		*
5.	GREEN	ORANGE		*
6.	BLUE	RED		*
7.	STAR	GREEN		*
8.	STAR	GREEN		*
9.	PLAID	STAR		*
10.	YELLOW	GREEN		*
11.	GREEN	BLUE		*
12.	BLUE	RED		*
13.	ORANGE	BLUE		*
14.	GREEN	ORANGE		*
15.	PLAID	ORANGE		*
16.	ORANGE	POLKA-DOT		*
17.	GREEN	BLUE		*
18.	POLKA-DOT	GREEN		*
19.	ORANGE	POLKA-DOT		*
20.	RED	POLKA-DOT		*
21.	GREEN	GREEN	*	
22.	BLUE	RED		*
23.	GREEN	POLKA-DOT		*
24.	POLKA-DOT	RED		*
25.	POLKA-DOT	POLKA-DOT	*	
26.	BLUE	RED		*
27.	GREEN	GREEN	*	
28.	POLKA-DOT	GREEN		*
29.	RED	ORANGE		*
30.	ORANGE	ORANGE	*	
31.	ORANGE	GREEN		*
32.	BLUE	POLKA-DOT		*

	Bucket	Spinner	W	L
33.	YELLOW	STAR		*
34.	BLUE	RED		*
35.	ORANGE	YELLOW		*
36.	ORANGE	GREEN		*
37.	BLUE	POLKA-DOT		*
38.	RED	YELLOW		*
39.	BLUE	GREEN		*
40.	ORANGE	GREEN		*
41.	ORANGE	ORANGE	*	
42.	RED	POLKA-DOT	*	
43.	POLKA-DOT	GREEN		*
44.	GREEN	POLKA-DOT		*
45.	POLKA-DOT	ORANGE		*
46.	GREEN	ORANGE		*
47.	BLUE	STAR		*
48.	GREEN	PLAID		*
49.	GREEN	ORANGE		*
50.	YELLOW	ORANGE		*
51.	GREEN	PLAID		*
52.	GREEN	ORANGE		*
53.	YELLOW	ORANGE		*
54.	RED	PLAID		*
55.	BLUE	ORANGE		*
56.	PLAID	GREEN		*
57.	ORANGE	ORANGE	*	
58.	GREEN	ORANGE		*
59.	POLKA-DOT	GREEN		*
60.	GREEN	BLUE		*
61.	ORANGE	BLUE		*
62.	BLUE	RED		*
63.	ORANGE	GREEN		*
64.	BLUE	RED		*
65.	PLAID	YELLOW		*
66.	POLKA-DOT	RED		

	Bucket	Spinner	W	L
67.	GREEN	BLUE		*
68.	YELLOW	BLUE		*
69.	RED	ORANGE		*
70.	RED	ORANGE		*
71.	POLKA-DOT	RED		*
72.	GREEN	POLKA-DOT		*
73.	BLUE	BLUE	*	
74.	BLUE	STAR		*
75.	GREEN	YELLOW		*
76.	BLUE	BLUE	*	
78.	GREEN	YELLOW		*
79.	BLUE	ORANGE		*
80.	BLUE	POLKA-DOT		*
81.	ORANGE	GREEN		*
82.	GREEN	RED		*
83.	PLAID	GREEN		*
84.	ORANGE	ORANGE	*	
85.	STAR	GREEN		*
86.	YELLOW	BLUE		*
87.	YELLOW	BLUE		*
88.	GREEN	BLUE		*
89.	GREEN	POLKA-DOT		*
90.	POLKA-DOT	STAR		*
91.	BLUE	GREEN		*
92.	BLUE	BLUE	*	
93.	ORANGE	YELLOW		*
94.	BLUE	BLUE	*	
95.	PLAID	GREEN		*
96.	RED	RED	*	
97.	POLKA-DOT	GREEN		*
98.	BLUE	RED		*
99.	GREEN	BLUE		*
100.	GREEN	BLUE		*

A Teacher's Comments

Each student in this group received the total of 9 points possible on their game design. Their rules were clear and easy to understand, their model was neat, they correctly concluded that the game would make a profit, and the game was easy to construct and use.

Susy received 12 of the 13 points possible for her written report. Her descriptions of why people would want to play the game and why this game should be chosen are somewhat general; for this I deducted 1 point. I also commented that Susy makes a small error in adding the results of the experiments (where she reports the total winning as $\frac{19}{100}$ rather than $\frac{15}{100}$), but I did not deduct for this error.

Heidi received 9 of the 13 points possible for her written report. I deducted 1 point for her comment that, from the group's experiments, the experimental probability of winning is approximately 5.5 out of 100 games, because this does not match the given data. Heidi gives the correct expected payout but she doesn't explain how she calculated it; 1 point was deducted for this. Another point was deducted because, although Heidi describes the data collection and presents the results, she does not connect that information to the probability of winning the game or the expected payout. A fourth point was deducted because of the effort the reader must expend to follow Heidi's report.

Using the self-assessment in each unit, students can reflect on the mathematics in the unit and write about what they have made sense of, what they are still struggling with, and how they contributed to the class's understanding of the mathematics in the unit. The three student papers shown on the following pages came from a single class and are examples of how students might approach the self-assessment. Work from these same three students using this same assessment tool can be found in the Assessment Resources section of the *Stretching and Shrinking* unit.

A Teacher's Comments

At the end of each unit, I assign the self-assessment. I collect these, read them, write comments to the students about what they have written, and sometimes discuss with my class general concerns I have that are common to several papers. I also talk individually with students if I can't make sense of something they have written or if they seem to be struggling and confused with several of the ideas with which we have been working.

Reviewing these papers, and others, from my class helps me to make instructional decisions as to things I will do with the students I presently have in class as well as what I will do when I teach the unit next year. I am amazed by just how difficult self-assessment has been for my students. We have made progress, but many of them still approach this as a task to be completed and not as an opportunity to self-reflect, to take stock in what they know and can do, and to express what they are still not making sense of.

For the last couple of units, I have been working with my students on their writing about the mathematics they have learned. My students are getting better at this but are not any better at *telling* me about their class participation. They continue to list actions they performed but fail to explain what ideas they actually contributed to the class. I am going to make a conscious effort to work on this with them. My casual remarks and written comments to them have not gotten me far. I need to make a more deliberate attempt to help them understand what my questions are asking of them and what I expect of them for a response.

Aimee's Self-Assessment

Aimee (and others) continues to write her self-assessment knowing that I have been a part of all the classroom experiences; she does not write as specifically as she should. It is as if she doesn't think she needs to because I should know what she means; I was there. She often lists things without explaining them. For example, she lists the tools she uses to determine theoretical probability but does not tell what theoretical probability is or how these tools help her determine theoretical probability. She also lists ways that she participates in class but does not explain what she actually said or demonstrated in class.

Aimee's lack of explanation and clarity is apparent in her section on Mathematical Ideas. She states, "I learned that to determine expected value you must know how much of something you are dealing with, for example how many games you are going to play. You also need to know the probability of winning or losing the game and how much profit you will make (or how much you will take in or pay out). Expected value is the amount that you can expect to get after a long time." Here, Aimee expects that the reader knows that in this unit we did several problems dealing with paying to play carnival games and winning or losing money at each game. She also expects that I know how these terms are related and can fill in the missing links and ideas.

I talked to one of the language arts teachers about this issue. She suggested that I again discuss the problem with the class and that together we rewrite the questions on the next self-assessment to include sentences that remind students to be more specific. For example, the class participation section might be rewritten as follows: "I contributed to the classroom discussion when I said _____. I helped myself and others in the class understand _____ when I said (or showed or did) _____."

Aimee

1. a) I have learned that to find theoretical probabilities (which is, in theory, based on mathematical reasoning and what is going to or should happen) by using a counting tree, an area model, an organized list, or a chart. I learned that experimental probability is to figure out the probability by looking at the data you collected in an experiment. I learned that to determine expected value, you must know how much of something you are dealing with, for example how many games you are going to play. You also need to know the probability of winning or losing the game, and how much profit you will make (or how much you will take in or pay out). Expected value is the amount that you can expect to get after a long time.

b) Page 21 in my journal shows that I know what expected value is and how to use it to find the long term average. Page 11 shows that I know how to use organized lists and charts to find the theoretical data. Page 33 shows that I know how to use a counting tree to find theoretical probability. Page 1 shows that I know how to find theoretical and experimental probability and how to use them.

2. a) The mathematical idea that I am still struggling with is the one of expected value. When we first started out learning about this I had a hard time understanding why it worked. Now I think that I understand why and how a little bit more.

b) I think this idea was difficult for me because I didn't really understand what you were dividing by what or why you were dividing these things. Now I am not struggling very much.

c) Page 30 is really the only page that clearly shows that I am confused in what to divide by what, but that I have grasped most of the concept of expected value.

Class Participation: I contributed to the discussion and understanding when we discussed the definitions of our vocabulary words. I helped to discuss the answers to many problems, particularly the ones using area models because I understood those very well. I tried to help others understand things, I just hope I didn't confuse them more.

Stacey's Self-Assessment

Stacey's self-assessment shows me some things she knows but also some things she thinks she knows but doesn't. She has made an error in listing and finding the theoretical probability of getting a match when pulling blocks from two bags, each containing seven blocks that are red, blue, or green. Her list and her probabilities suggest that the first bag holds only three blocks, one red, one blue, and one green; or contain the same number of red, blue, and green blocks. Neither of these situations matches what is described in her writing. This misconception is interesting to me as a teacher because Stacey chose this as an example of what she knows. I will talk with her about this.

Stacey's paper also contains a statement that makes me think that she either doesn't think that experimental probability is a "real" probability or that she doesn't put much faith in it. She says, "It's what happens when you try the situation. It may or may not be the same to the probability." I am uncertain what she is thinking about here. I plan to discuss theoretical and experimental probability with the class when I return their papers. I will note her comments and make sure that I call on her and ask her to talk about experimental probability and what it means and tells us.

Like Aimee, Stacey writes as if she does not have to be clear and give much detail because she is writing to me and I was in class with her every day. She also does not give specific examples of how she contributed to the class.

Stacey

1. To find theoritical probability you can do many things. One of them is a matrix chart which is simmalar to finding cooridinates on graph. Area models are also useful for situations such as going through paths with forks. Another way to find probability is by listing.
Example: there's 2 bags of blocks. In 1 bag there's 2 red, 3 blue, 2 green. If you match you win a prize. In Bag2 3 red, 2 blue, 2 green. You can make a list:

Red - Ⓡ Green - R. Blue - R.
     Ⓡ   P.   R.
     Ⓡ   R.   R.
     B.   B.   Ⓑ
     B.   B.   Ⓑ
     G.   Ⓖ   G.
     G.   Ⓖ   G.

The probability of mathes in 1/3 of 7/21. There was 21 possibilities and 7 mathes (winners). You can make a diagram in situations such as making free throws. If Kate is a 70% free-throw shotter in a 2-shot situation:
1st I marked of 70% of the grid (7/10) because Kate has a 70% chance of making both shots. Then I took 3/10 of the area left and marked that off as 1 point. The rest was 0.
Probability of Kate's shooting:

2 points - 49%   Theoretical probability
1 point - 42%   is what's expected to
0 points - 9%   happen.

To find experimental probability you just have to do the experiment. It's what happens when you try the situation. It may or may not be the same to the probability.
b) found on prob. 6.3 + prob 4.1, pages 15 + 21
2 a) Mathematical ideas I'm still struggling about is finding probability when you do not replace blocks after drawn.
b) This is confusing because it's new to me. It's sometimes hard to find theoretical probabilities.
c) On page 23 This shows notes of how to find it + the work shown.

Class Participation

In problem 4.1 I discussed with my table partners and shared my ideas. Also in class disscussion 2.1 (chances with dice).

Susy's Self-Assessment

Susy's examples are thorough. I will make a transparency of these and share them with the class as an example of good work. I try to do this as often as possible to help my students understand what the assessment tool is asking them to do and to understand what I consider standards of good work.

Susy's writing for the Mathematical Ideas section suggests to me that she is struggling with expected value. She is not alone. Several of my students' papers show that they are struggling with this idea. This really doesn't surprise me, as this is a difficult concept. I will use this information and will find ways to have my students deal with this idea throughout the rest of the year, such as including questions about expected value when I make up a review sheet. (These I write myself and have my students do an average of once a month.) I will also use problems that deal with expected value as class openers. (These are one-question problems that I use to start class a couple of days each week. My opener problems usually do not deal with the specific mathematical topic we are studying at the time. I use them as opportunities for my students to reflect on ideas we have discussed earlier in the year.)

When I teach this unit next year, I want to remember that my students had difficulty with the idea of expected value and be more conscious of what sense my students are making of it. To help me remember that expected value was problematic for my students, I will mark my teacher's edition and write notes to myself while it is fresh in my mind.

Susy

1. a.) In the unit we have studied I have learned that propability is the chance that an event will occur. It can be writing in a fraction or words. When it is writen as a fraction you read the numerator as the chance it occured, over the denominator, the amount of chances there is possibal. Example: If you have 2 green cubes in a bucket with a total of 10 cubes, The probibility of getting green is 2/10. A probibility of 1 means it is certain a thing will happen. A probibilty of 0 means it is impossibal to happen. You will never draw a blue cubes from a bucket that is all red cubes, so the possibility that will happen is 0%. Probability is also used to find the expected average of something happening. This means you

can find a close guess at how often an event will occur. If you are shooting free throws you will be able to determine your expected value after you shoot a couple. You find it by adding up the points you made and dividing by how many trials you did. This gives you an average you can expect to come close to your acualle outcome. Probibility helps me when I play basketball, because by knowing how to find the expected average I can estimate about how many free throws I will make.
b.) You can find evidence in my journal on problem 2.2, quiz A, problem 5.2, Inv. 5 ACE, problems 6.1-6.3 and Inv. 6 ACE. These show that I have a pretty good understanding of probibiliy and how to find it. Problem 2.2 shows my ability to calculate probability and

use it to test a prediction. Quiz A shows that I know how to use theoretacal probibility to determin a fair amount of points, and how to find theoretitcal probability. Problem 5.2 shows I can find expected average in free throw situations. Inv. 5 ACE also does this. Problems 6.1-6.3 show I can analyze games and find if they are fair, and that I can find theoritical probability.

2. a.) I am still struggling with expected average and long term average.
b.) I sometimes don't understand how they can be calculated.
c.) Problems 5.1, 5.2, and 6.1 show I do not completly understand this in the unit.

I contributed by explaining my answers to problems. I asked questions on issues I did not understand. I sometimes asked students to describe their answers in a different way.

Blackline Masters

Match/No-Match

Turn number	Result	Player A's score	Player B's score
1			
2			
3			
4			
5			
6			
7			
8			
9			
10			
11			
12			

Turn number	Result	Player A's score	Player B's score
13			
14			
15			
16			
17			
18			
19			
20			
21			
22			
23			
24			

Making Purple

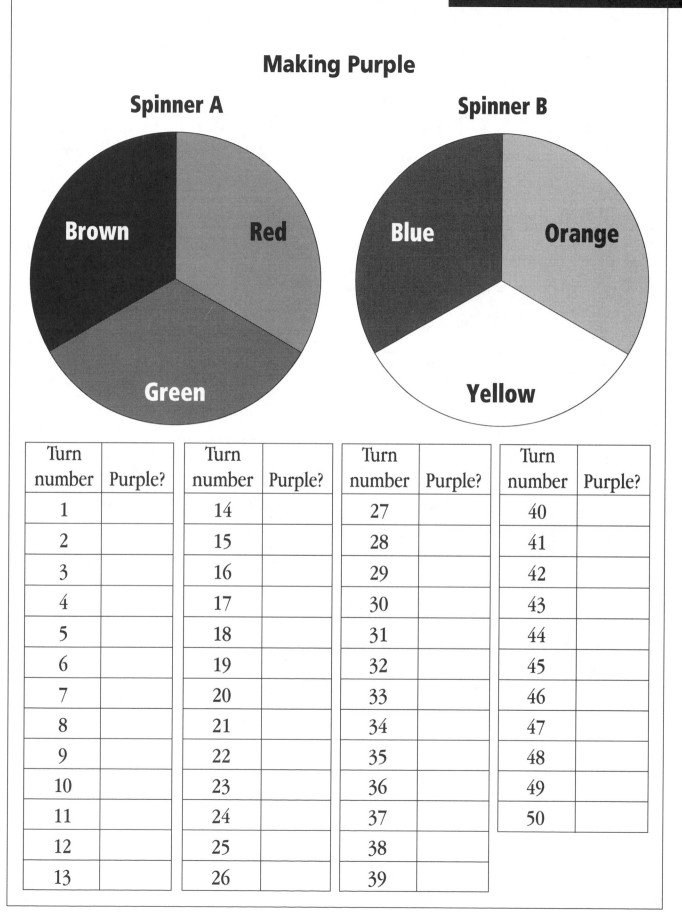

Spinner A

Brown
Red
Green

Spinner B

Blue
Orange
Yellow

Turn number	Purple?
1	
2	
3	
4	
5	
6	
7	
8	
9	
10	
11	
12	
13	

Turn number	Purple?
14	
15	
16	
17	
18	
19	
20	
21	
22	
23	
24	
25	
26	

Turn number	Purple?
27	
28	
29	
30	
31	
32	
33	
34	
35	
36	
37	
38	
39	

Turn number	Purple?
40	
41	
42	
43	
44	
45	
46	
47	
48	
49	
50	

The Addition Game

Roll number	Sum	Odd or even?
1		
2		
3		
4		
5		
6		
7		
8		
9		
10		
11		
12		
13		
14		
15		
16		
17		
18		

Roll number	Sum	Odd or even?
19		
20		
21		
22		
23		
24		
25		
26		
27		
28		
29		
30		
31		
32		
33		
34		
35		
36		

The Multiplication Game

Roll number	Product	Odd or even?	Roll number	Product	Odd or even?
1			19		
2			20		
3			21		
4			22		
5			23		
6			24		
7			25		
8			26		
9			27		
10			28		
11			29		
12			30		
13			31		
14			32		
15			33		
16			34		
17			35		
18			36		

Spinners for 60% Free-Throw Shooter

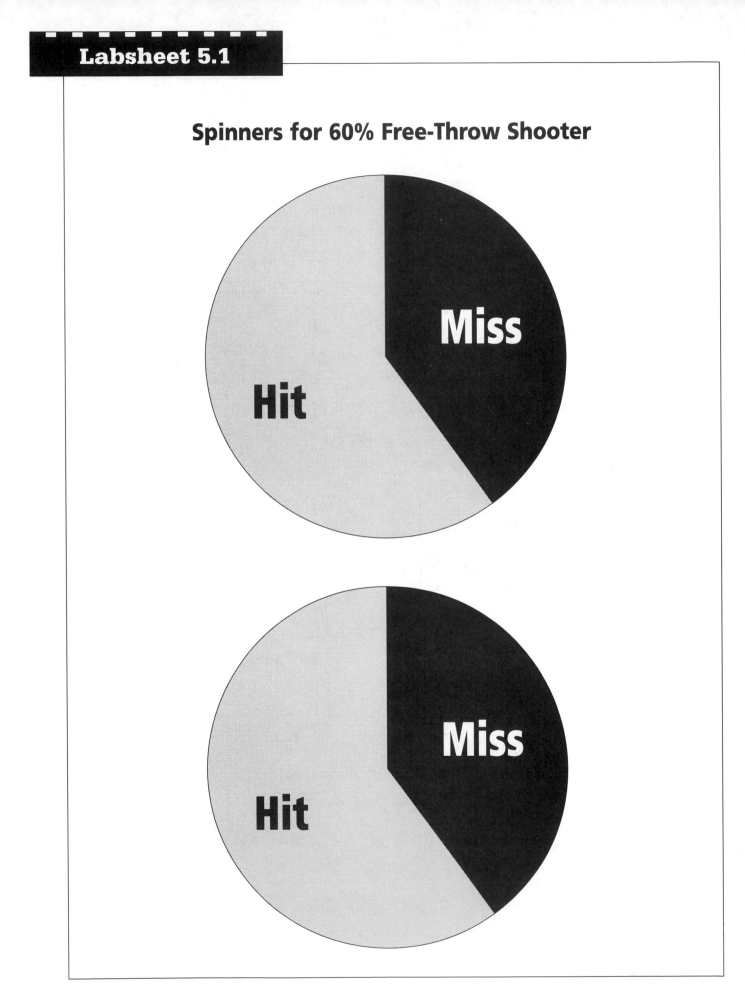

One-and-One Free-Throw Shooters

For each player, use the grid to analyze the problem
and answer the questions.

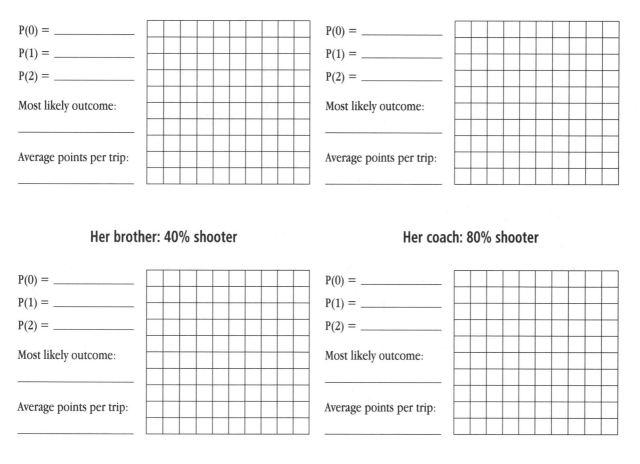

Nicky: 60% shooter

P(0) = _____

P(1) = _____

P(2) = _____

Most likely outcome:

_____

Average points per trip:

_____

Her 8-year-old cousin: 20% shooter

P(0) = _____

P(1) = _____

P(2) = _____

Most likely outcome:

_____

Average points per trip:

_____

Her brother: 40% shooter

P(0) = _____

P(1) = _____

P(2) = _____

Most likely outcome:

_____

Average points per trip:

_____

Her coach: 80% shooter

P(0) = _____

P(1) = _____

P(2) = _____

Most likely outcome:

_____

Average points per trip:

_____

Summary Table

Shooter's average	P(0 points)	P(1 point)	P(2 points)	Average points per trip
$\frac{2}{10} = 20\%$				
$\frac{4}{10} = 40\%$				
$\frac{6}{10} = 60\%$				
$\frac{8}{10} = 80\%$				

Animal Olympics Quiz Results

Below are the results from two classes who took the test. Everyone guessed on every question.

TTFT	TFTF	TTTT	FTFF	FFTF	TFTF
FFTT	TTFF	TFTT	TTTF	FFTT	FFTF
TFFT	FFTT	TFTF	FTFT	TFFF	FTFF
FFFF	FTTF	FTTT	TFFF	FFFT	FFTF
TFFF	FTTT	FTTF	FFFT	TFTF	TTTF
TFTT	FTTF	TFFF	TTFF	FFTT	TFTF
TTFF	FTFT	TFFF	FTFT	TTTF	FTTT
TTFT	FFFT	TFFT	TFFF	FTTF	TFTT
TTTF	FFFF	FFTT	FFTF	TFTF	TFFT
TTTT	FFFT	FTFF	TTTT	TFFT	FFFF

A. How many blocks drawn by your class were blue? Yellow? Red?

B. Which color block—blue, yellow, or red—do you think there are the greatest number of in the bucket? The least number of?

C. Based on your experimental data, predict the fraction of blocks in the bucket that are blue, that are yellow, and that are red.

D. After your teacher shows you the blocks in the bucket, find the fraction of blue blocks, of yellow blocks, and of red blocks.

E. How do the fractions of blocks that are blue, yellow, and red compare to the fractions of blue, yellow, and red blocks drawn during the experiment?

A. Use the results you collected to find the *experimental probabilities* of a match and a no-match. The experimental probability of a match is

$$P(\text{match}) = \frac{\text{number of turns that are matches}}{\text{total number of turns}}$$

The experimental probability of a no-match is

$$P(\text{no-match}) = \frac{\text{number of turns that are no-matches}}{\text{total number of turns}}$$

B. List all the possible outcomes of a turn (two spins). Use your list to determine the *theoretical probabilities* of a match and a no-match. Since all the outcomes are equally likely, the theoretical probability of a match is

$$P(\text{match}) = \frac{\text{number of outcomes that are matches}}{\text{number of possible outcomes}}$$

The theoretical probability of a no-match is

$$P(\text{no-match}) = \frac{\text{number of outcomes that are no-matches}}{\text{number of possible outcomes}}$$

C. How do your results for parts A and B compare?

D. Is Match/No-Match a fair game? If you think the game is fair, explain why. If you think it is not fair, explain how the rules could be changed to make it fair.

A. Play Making Purple 50 times, and record the results of each turn. Based on your results, what is the experimental probability that a player will "make purple" on any single turn?

B. Plot the experimental probability of making purple you would have found if you had stopped after 5 turns, 10 turns, 15 turns, and so on, up to 50 turns.

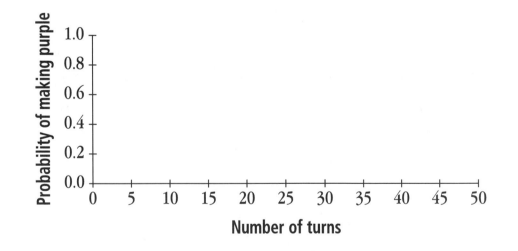

C. What do you think your graph would look like if you had taken 100 turns? 200 turns? 1000 turns?

D. List the possible outcomes for a turn. Write the outcomes as pairs of the form *color on spinner A/color on spinner B.* Are the outcomes equally likely? Explain why or why not.

E. What is the theoretical probability that a player will make purple on a turn?

F. How does the experimental probability of making purple compare with the theoretical probability of making purple? Explain.

April and Tioko decide to play the Match/No-Match game on the spinner below. As in the original game, a turn consists of two spins. Player A scores 1 point if the spins match, and Player B scores 1 point if they do not match.

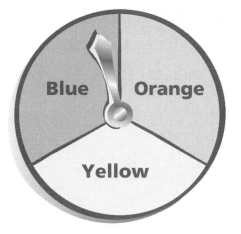

A. Use a counting tree to find all the possible outcomes for this game.

B. What is the theoretical probability of getting a match on a turn?

C. What is the theoretical probability of getting a no-match on a turn?

D. Do you think this is a fair game? If you think the game is fair, explain why. If you think it is not fair, explain how the rules could be changed to make it fair.

Play the Addition Game with a partner. Keep track of your results.

A. Based on your data, what is the experimental probability of rolling an odd sum? An even sum?

B. List all the possible pairs of numbers you can roll with two number cubes.

C. What is the theoretical probability of rolling an odd sum? An even sum?

D. Do you think the Addition Game is a fair game? Explain why or why not.

Play the Multiplication Game with a partner. Keep track of your results.

A. Based on your data, what is the experimental probability of rolling an odd product? An even product?

B. What is the theoretical probability of rolling an odd product? An even product?

C. Do you think the Multiplication Game is fair? Explain why or why not.

D. If the game consisted of 100 rolls instead of 36, how many points would you expect each player to have at the end of the game?

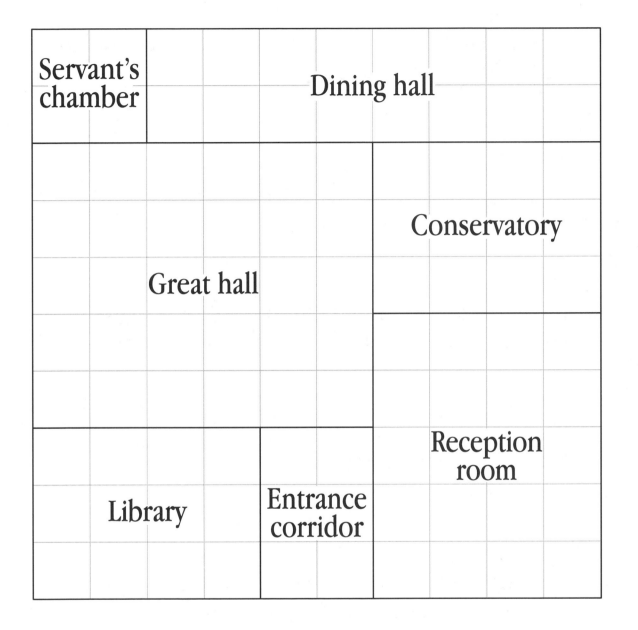

A. How can this information about how the computer hides the treasure help you find the treasure?

B. You have just entered level 1 of Treasure Hunt. What is the probability that the treasure is hidden in the great hall?

In the servant's chamber?

C. If you play level 1 ten times, how many times can you expect the treasure to be hidden in the great hall?

In the servant's chamber?

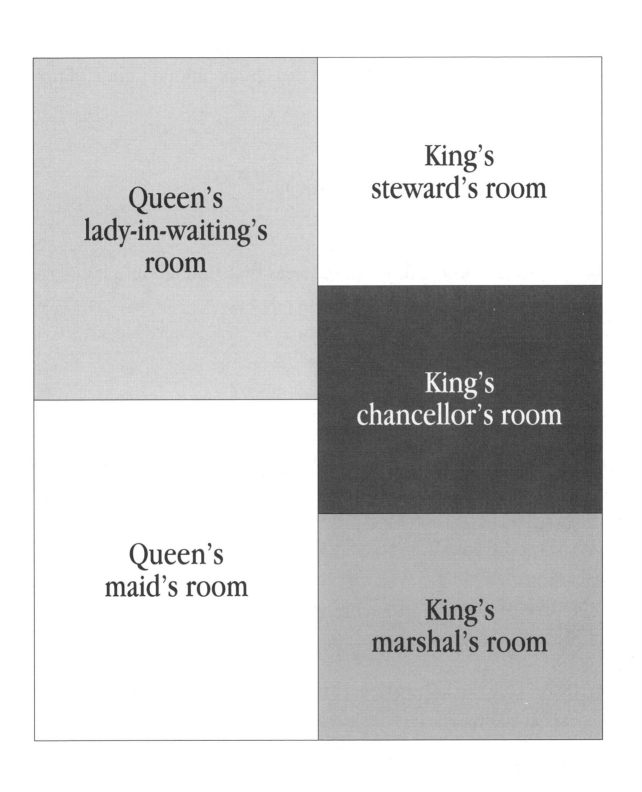

Queen's
lady-in-waiting's
room

King's
steward's room

King's
chancellor's room

Queen's
maid's room

King's
marshal's room

A. What is the probability that the treasure is hidden in one of the queen's servants' rooms?

In one of the king's servants' rooms?

B. What is the probability that the treasure is hidden in the maid's room?

In the steward's room?

C. If you play the second level 100 times, how many times can you expect the treasure to be hidden in one of the queen's servants' rooms?

In one of the king's servants' rooms?

D. If you play the second level 100 times, how many times can you expect the treasure to be hidden in the maid's room?

In the steward's room?

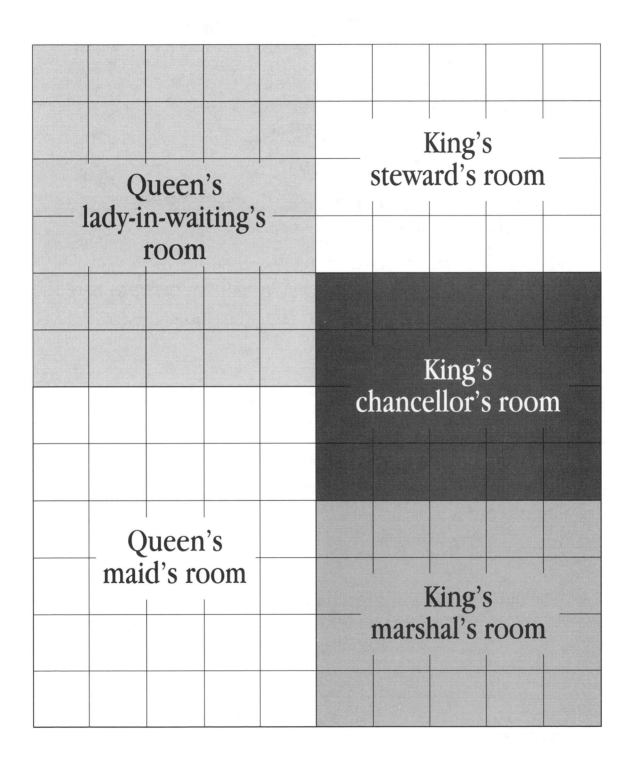

Queen's
lady-in-waiting's
room

King's
steward's room

King's
chancellor's room

Queen's
maid's room

King's
marshal's room

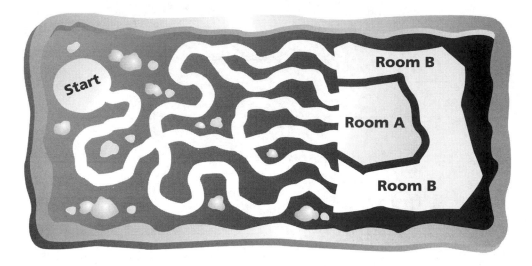

A. In which room would you put the treasure in order to have the best chance of beating Zark? Explain your choice.

B. Work with a partner to find a way to simulate Deep in the Dungeon so it can be played without a computer. You will need to figure out a way for Zark to make a random selection at each fork.

C. Play your simulation of Deep in the Dungeon 20 times with your partner. Take turns hiding the treasure and playing Zark. For each game, record the room that Zark ends in.

D. Based on your results from part C, what is the experimental probability that Zark will end in room A? What is the experimental probability that Zark will end in room B?

A. List all the different ways Brianna can place the four marbles in the two containers.

B. Which arrangement will give Brianna and Emmanuel the best chance of winning? Explain why the arrangement you chose is the best.

C. For the arrangement you chose, what is the probability of drawing an orange marble?

A. Which of the following do you think is most likely to happen?

- Nicky will score 0 points. That is, she will miss the first shot.
- Nicky will score 1 point. That is, she will make the first shot and miss the second shot.
- Nicky will score 2 points. That is, she will make two shots.

Record what you think before you analyze the situation.

B. Plan a way to simulate this situation. Describe your plan.

C. Use your plan from part B to simulate Nicky's one-and-one situation 20 times. Record the result of each trial.

D. Based on your results, what is the experimental probability that Nicky will score 0 points? 1 point? 2 points?

E. Make an area model for this situation, using a 10 by 10 grid. What is the theoretical probability that Nicky will score 0 points? 1 point? 2 points?

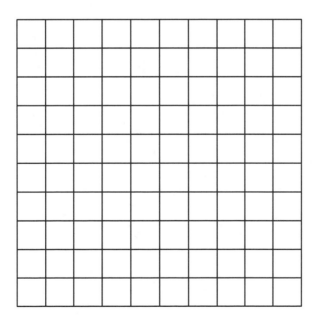

F. How do the three theoretical probabilities compare with the three experimental probabilities?

Suppose Nicky has a 60% free-throw average and is in a one-and-one free-throw situation 100 times during the season.

A. What total number of points would you expect Nicky to score in these 100 trips to the free-throw line?

B. What would Nicky's average number of points per trip be? This is the **expected value** for this situation.

A. Play each game 20 times. Record your results on the board so everyone has access to the class data.

B. Based on the class data, if 100 people play Julie's game, how many people would you expect to win?

C. If 100 people play Li Fong's game, how many people would you expect to win?

A. What is the theoretical probability of winning Fergus's game? Explain how you got your answer.

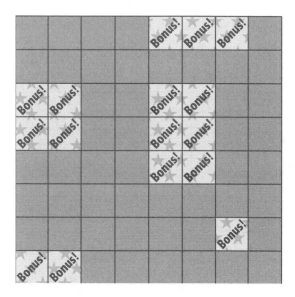

B. What is the theoretical probability of winning Judi's game? Explain how you got your answer.

The carnival committee is trying to decide which version of the game to use for the carnival. For each version, answer parts A–D.

A. How much money will the school take in if the game is played 100 times?

B. How much money can the school expect to pay out in prizes if the game is played 100 times?

C. What is the average amount the school will pay out each time the game is played?

D. If the game is played 100 times, will the school make money or lose money?

A. List all the possible combinations of female and male puppies Scout might have. Assume that for each puppy, a male and a female are equally likely.

B. Is Scout more likely to have four male puppies, or two male puppies and two female puppies? Explain your reasoning.

C. Is Scout more likely to have four male puppies, or a female puppy, a male puppy, a female puppy, and a male puppy, in that order? Explain your reasoning.

TTFT	TFTF	TTTT	FTFF	FFTF	TFTF
FFTT	TTFF	TFTT	TTTF	FFTT	FFTF
TFFT	FFTT	TFTF	FTFT	TFFF	FTFF
FFFF	FTTF	FTTT	TFFF	FFFT	FFTF
TFFF	FTTT	FTTF	FFFT	TFTF	TTTF
TFTT	FTTF	TFFF	TTFF	FFTT	TFTF
TTFF	FTFT	TFFF	FTFT	TTTF	FTTT
TTFT	FFFT	TFFT	TFFF	FTTF	TFTT
TTTF	FFFF	FFTT	FFTF	TFTF	TFFT
TTTT	FFFT	FTFF	TTTT	TFFT	FFFF

A. Using the data above, what is the experimental probability that someone who guesses every answer will get all four answers right?

B. What is the experimental probability that someone who guesses every answer will get exactly three answers right?

C. What is the experimental probability that someone who guesses every answer will get exactly two answers right?

D. What is the experimental probability that someone who guesses every answer will get exactly one answer right?

E. What is the experimental probability that someone who guesses every answer will get no answers right?

Animal Olympics Quiz

1. The fastest-flying bird is the peregrine falcon, which can fly a maximum of 217 miles per hour when swooping downward at a 45 degree angle. *(true)*

2. The best dog "sniffers" in the world are Belgian sheepdogs named Rocky and Barco. They have helped make 969 drug seizures worth $182,000. *(false; the drugs were actually worth $182,000,000)*

3. The canine high-jump record is held by a German shepherd dog named Volse, who jumped 11 feet, 9 inches in France, in 1989. *(true)*

4. The best cat climber in the world was a four-month-old kitten who followed a group of climbers to the top of the 14,691-foot Matterhorn in the Swiss Alps. *(true)*

(Source: *Guinness Book of Records 1994.* Ed. Peter Matthews. New York: Bantam Books, 1994.)

Dear Family,

The next unit in your child's course of study in mathematics class this year is *What Do You Expect?* This unit is about the concepts of probability and will help students understand common ideas that they read or hear about every day. They will explore long-range expectations in probability situations and learn how to make better predictions.

In the unit, students will meet Nicky, a basketball player who has a 60% free-throw average. They will analyze the probability that she will succeed in her free-throw attempts in different kinds of situations. This is just one of many interesting situations that students will explore in this unit.

Here are some strategies for helping your child work with the ideas in this unit:

- Situations involving probability are all around us. When you notice such a use in a newspaper, a magazine, or on television, talk about it with your child. Ask whether he or she wants to share the usage in class as an example for the other students.

- Help your child to keep track of the local weather in your area for a week and make notes about how accurate a particular forecaster's predictions are. Talk with your child about his or her results.

- Look at your child's mathematics notebook. You may want to review the section where your child is recording definitions for new words that he or she is encountering in the unit.

- Encourage your child's efforts in completing all homework assignments.

If you have any questions or concerns about this unit or your child's progress in the class, please feel free to call. We are interested in your child's success in mathematics.

Sincerely,

Estimada familia,

La próxima unidad del programa de matemáticas de su hijo o hija para este curso se llama *What Do You Expect?* (¿Qué esperas?). La misma trata sobre los conceptos de la probabilidad y ayudará a los alumnos a entender mejor ideas muy comunes que leen y escuchan todos los días. Así, explorarán las expectativas a largo plazo de las situaciones de probabilidad y aprenderán a hacer predicciones más acertadas.

En la presente unidad los alumnos conocerán a Nicky, jugadora de básquetbol que acierta un promedio del 60% de sus tiros libres. Examinarán la probabilidad de que enceste sus tiros libres en una amplia diversidad de situaciones. Se trata de tan sólo una de las numerosas e interesantes situaciones que explorarán en esta unidad.

He aquí algunas estrategias que ustedes pueden emplear para ayudar a su hijo o hija con las ideas de esta unidad:

- Las situaciones relacionadas con la probabilidad son muy comunes en nuestro entorno. Cuando observen una de ellas en un periódico, una revista o en la televisión, coméntenla con su hijo o hija. Pregúntenle si quiere exponerla en clase como ejemplo para los demás alumnos.

- Ayúdenle a observar el tiempo local durante una semana y a tomar notas sobre la exactitud de las predicciones de un meteorólogo determinado. Hablen con su hijo o hija sobre los resultados.

- Miren su cuaderno de matemáticas. Es recomendable que repasen la sección en la que anota las definiciones de las nuevas palabras que encuentra en la unidad.

- Anímenle a esforzarse para que complete toda la tarea.

Si ustedes necesitan más detalles o aclaraciones respecto a la unidad o sobre los progresos de su hijo o hija en esta clase, no duden en llamarnos. Nos interesa que su hijo o hija avance en el estudio de las matemáticas.

Atentamente,

Small 10 by 10 Grids

What Do You Expect?

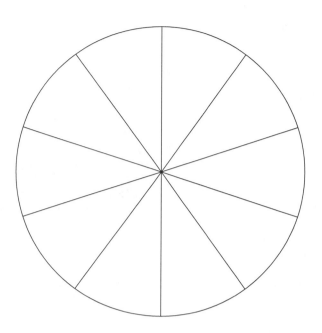

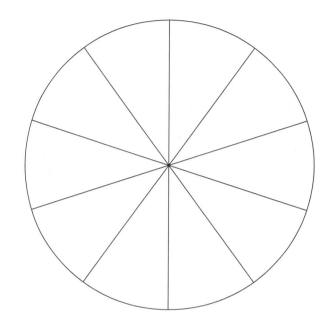

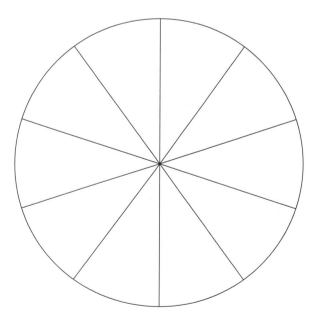

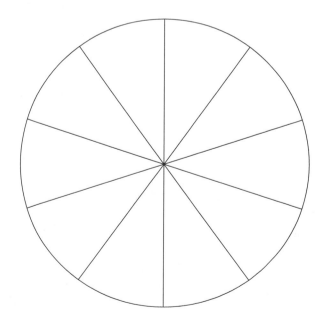

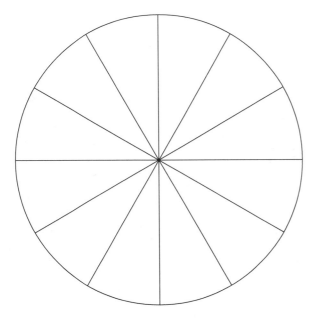

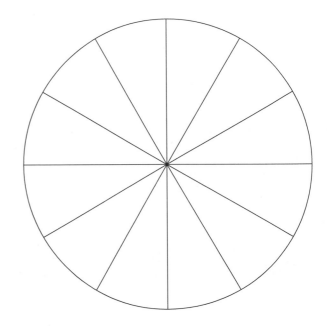

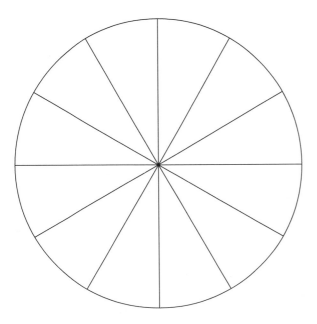

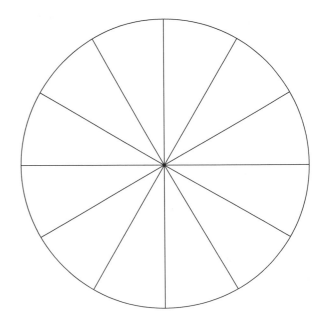

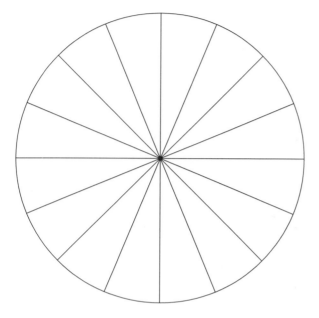
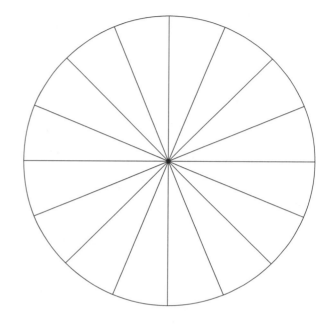
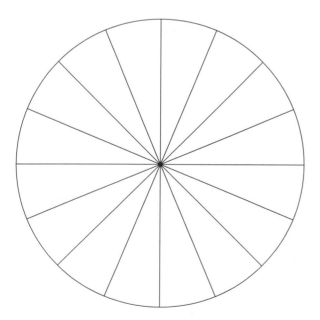
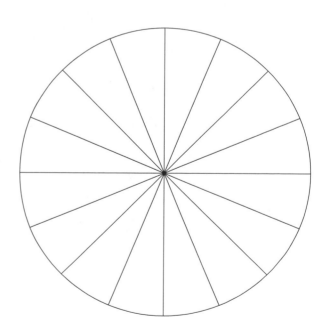

What Do You Expect?

Grid Paper

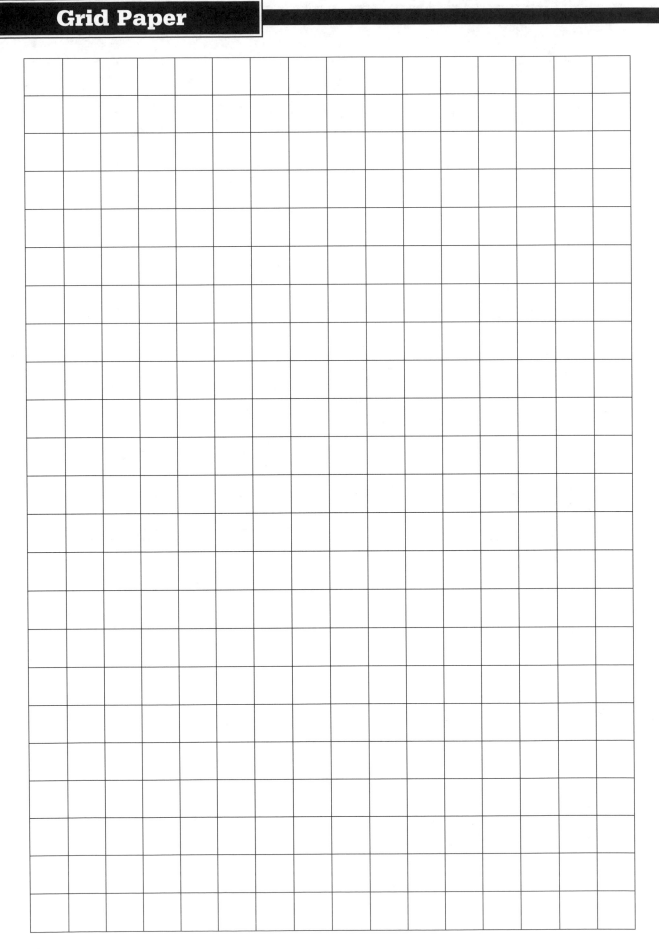

Additional Practice

Investigation 1

Use these problems for additional practice after Investigation 1.

1. Josh is playing golf. He has 3 white golf balls, 4 yellow golf balls, and 1 red golf ball in his golf bag. At the first hole, he randomly draws a ball from his bag.

   a. What is the probability that he draws a white golf ball?

   b. What is the probability that he draws a red golf ball?

   c. What is the probability that he draws a yellow golf ball?

   d. On the sixth hole, Josh drives one of his white golf balls into a pond and has to draw another ball from his bag.

      i. What is the probability that he draws a white golf ball?

      ii. What is the probability that he draws a red golf ball?

      iii. What is the probability that he draws a yellow golf ball?

   e. Are the probabilities you found in parts a–d experimental probabilities or theoretical probabilities? Explain your reasoning.

2. To help his 3-year-old sister Emily learn her colors, Kyle has put some yellow, green, red, and blue blocks in a bucket. Emily draws a block from the bucket, names its color, and puts the block back in the bucket. Then Kyle mixes the blocks, and Emily draws again. In playing this game 20 times, Emily draws a yellow block 6 times, a green block 2 times, a red block 8 times, and a blue block 4 times.

   a. Based on Emily's draws, what is the probability of drawing a yellow block from the bucket?

   b. What is the probability of drawing a green block from the bucket?

   c. What is the probability of drawing a red block from the bucket?

   d. What is the probability of drawing a blue block from the bucket?

   e. Are the probabilities you found in parts a–d experimental probabilities or theoretical probabilities? Explain your reasoning.

   f. There are a total of 10 blocks in the bucket. Based on the results of Emily's 20 draws, how many yellow, green, red, and blue blocks would you expect to be in the bucket? Explain your reasoning.

3. Juanita is holding five coins with a total value of 27 cents.

   a. What is the probability that three of the coins are pennies? Explain your reasoning.

   b. What is the probability that one of the coins is a quarter? Explain your reasoning.

4. Michelle flips a penny four times, and it lands heads up all four times. On her fifth flip, what is the probability that the penny will land tails up? Explain your reasoning.

Investigation 2

Use these problems for additional practice after Investigation 2.

1. A 4-sided die is a pyramid with four faces that are congruent equilateral triangles. The shape of a 4-sided die is also called a *tetrahedron*.

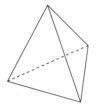

The faces of a 4-sided die are labeled with the numbers 1, 2, 3, and 4. A roll of a 4-sided die is determined by the number on the face the die lands on. Below are the rules of a game played with two 4-sided dice.

   • Player I and Player II take turns rolling two 4-sided dice.

   • If the sum of the numbers rolled is odd, Player I gets a point.

   • If the sum of the numbers rolled is even, Player II gets a point.

   • The player with the most points after 32 rolls wins.

   a. Make a table that shows all the possible outcomes of rolling two 4-sided dice.

   b. What is the probability of rolling a sum of 5?

   c. What is the probability of rolling a sum of 4?

   d. What is the probability of rolling a sum of 7?

   e. Do you think the game is fair? Explain your reasoning.

   f. Suppose that, in 32 rolls, a sum of 8 is rolled twice. Would you consider this unusual? Explain your reasoning.

2. A standard deck of playing cards has 52 cards. The deck is divided into 4 *suits*: spades, hearts, diamonds, and clubs. There are 13 cards of each suit.

   a. If you randomly draw a card from a standard deck of playing cards, what is the probability that you will draw a heart?

   b. If you draw 12 cards, how many clubs could you expect to draw? Explain your reasoning.

   c. If you remove all the diamonds from a deck of cards and then draw 12 cards, how many clubs could you expect to draw? Explain your reasoning.

   d. Are the probabilities you found in parts a–c experimental probabilities or theoretical probabilities? Explain your reasoning.

Investigation 3

Use these problems for additional practice after Investigation 3.

1. Shawon has a spinner that is divided into four regions. He spins the spinner several times and records his results in a table.

Region	Number of times spinner lands in region
1	9
2	4
3	12
4	11

    a. Based on Shawon's results, what is the probability of the spinner landing on region 1?

    b. What is the probability of the spinner landing on region 2?

    c. What is the probability of the spinner landing on region 3?

    d. What is the probability of the spinner landing on region 4?

    e. Are the probabilities you found in parts a–d theoretical probabilities or experimental probabilities?

    f. Make a drawing of what Shawon's spinner might look like.

2. Irene randomly tosses a cube onto the grid below.

    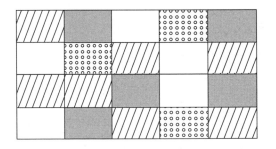

    a. What is the probability of the cube landing on a striped rectangle? Express your answer as a percent.

    b. What is the probability of the cube landing on a white rectangle? Express your answer as a percent.

    c. What is the probability of the cube landing on a gray rectangle? Express your answer as a percent.

    d. What is the probability of the cube landing on a dotted rectangle? Express your answer as a percent.

    e. What is the probability of the cube *not* landing on a white rectangle? Express your answer as a percent.

    f. What is the probability of the cube *not* landing on a striped rectangle? Express your answer as a percent.

    g. Irene proposed the following game: If the cube lands on a striped square or a dotted square, Irene wins; if the cube lands on a white square or a gray square, Irene's sister wins. Is this a fair game? Explain your reasoning.

Investigation 4

Use these problems for additional practice after Investigation 4.

1. Zark randomly selects one of the segments leading from point A. He follows that segment until he reaches another lettered point. Then, he randomly selects one of the segments leading from that point and follows it to the next lettered point. He continues this process until he reaches a dead end. In parts a–e below, we use a series of letters to represent a path. For example, the path *AEHI* is the path from *A* to *E* to *H* to *I*. Use the diagram to answer the following questions.

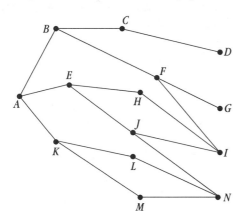

a. What is the probability that Zark followed path *AEJN*?

b. What is the probability that he followed path *ABCD*?

c. What is the probability that he followed path *ABFI*?

d. Are paths *AKLN* and *AKMN* equally likely to be selected? Explain your reasoning.

e. If Zark repeats this process 50 times, how many times would you expect him to follow path *AEJI*? Explain your reasoning.

2. a. If a letter is randomly selected from the letters A, B, C, D, and E, what is the probability that the letter will be B? Explain your reasoning.

b. If a letter is selected by spinning the spinner below, what is the probability that the letter will be B? Explain your reasoning.

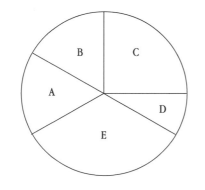

    c. Are your answers to parts a and b the same? Explain why or why not.

    d. If the spinner is spun once, what is the probability that it will *not* land in region C? Explain your reasoning.

    e. If the spinner is spun once, what is the probability that it will land in region D? Explain your reasoning.

    f. If the spinner is spun 100 times, how many times would you expect it to land in region E? Explain your reasoning.

3. The faces of one six-sided number cube are labeled 1, 1, 1, 2, 2, 3, and the faces of a second cube are labeled 0, 1, 2, 2, 2, 3. The two cubes are rolled, and the results are added.

    a. What is the probability of rolling a sum of 1?

    b. What is the probability of rolling a sum of 6?

    c. What is the probability of rolling a sum of 4?

    d. What is the probability of rolling a sum that is *not* 1 or 6? Explain your reasoning.

Investigation 5

Use these problems for additional practice after Investigation 5.

1. Jennifer is on her school's softball team. So far this season, Jennifer has 38 hits in 75 times at bat.

   a. Based on her current batting average, what are Jennifer's chances of getting a hit next time she is at bat? Explain your reasoning.

   b. If Jennifer bats 5 times during a game, how many hits would you expect her to get? Explain your reasoning.

   c. Next season, Jennifer wants to average 6 hits for every 10 times at bat. If she bats 80 times during the season, how many hits will she need to get to achieve her goal?

2. Aaron bowls on his school's bowling team. Based on statistics from past games, the probability that Aaron will knock down all ten pins on his first ball (a *strike*) is $\frac{2}{5}$. If he does not get a strike, the probability that he will knock down the remaining pins with his second ball (a *spare*) is $\frac{3}{4}$.

   a. In bowling, a *turkey* is three strikes in a row. If Aaron bowls three turns, what is the probability that he will get a turkey?

   b. Aaron had 8 chances to make spares during one of his league games. How many of the spares would you expect him to have made? Explain your reasoning.

   c. In bowling, an *open* occurs when the bowler does not get a strike on the first ball and then does not get a spare on the second ball. When Aaron rolls two balls, what are his chances of getting an open?

   d. Suppose Aaron bowls 30 practice frames. When he does not get a strike, he tries to get a spare.

      i. How many strikes would you expect Aaron to get?

      ii. How many spares would you expect Aaron to get?

      iii. How many opens would you expect Aaron to get?

Investigation 6

Use these problems for additional practice after Investigation 6.

1. In the Arithmacube game, two players take turns rolling two six-sided number cubes, each numbered 1 to 6. The numbers are added, and the sum is multiplied by 6. If the final result is an odd number, Player I gets 1 point. If the final result is an even number, Player II gets 1 point.

    a. List all the possible outcomes of a turn (that is, list the final results when the sum of two number cubes is multiplied by 6).

    b. What is the probability that the final number will be odd? What is the probability that the final number will be even? Explain your reasoning.

    c. Is this a fair game?

2. The Alphabet Game costs $0.25 to play. Before the game, 26 slips of paper, each with a different letter of the alphabet on it, are put into a bag. A player draws one slip from the bag. If the player draws a vowel (A, E, I, O, or U), he or she wins $1.

    a. What is the probability of winning the game?

    b. What is the probability of losing the game?

    c. If a player plays the Alphabet Game 26 times, how much money would you expect the player to win or lose? Explain your reasoning.

3. The Grid Game costs $1 to play. A player rolls a six-sided number cube twice. The first roll determines the *x*-coordinate of a point, and the second roll determines the *y*-coordinate. If the coordinates rolled are the coordinates of one of the points marked on the grid below, the player wins $4.

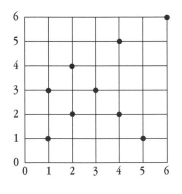

    a. What is the probability of winning the Grid Game?

    b. If a player plays the Grid Game 20 times, how much money would you expect the player to win or lose? Explain your reasoning.

    c. Is the Grid Game a fair game? Explain your reasoning.

Investigation 7

Use these problems for additional practice after Investigation 7.

1. Kathy runs cross country and plays basketball and softball. For each sport, she received a uniform with a randomly assigned number between 0 and 99 printed on it.

    a. What is the probability that all of Kathy's uniforms have odd numbers? Explain your reasoning.

    b. What is the probability that all of Kathy's uniforms have even numbers? Explain your reasoning.

    c. What is the probability that one of Kathy's uniforms has an even number and the other two have odd numbers? Explain your reasoning.

2. To play the Nickel Game, a player tosses two nickels at the same time. If both nickels land tails up, the player wins $1. If both nickels land heads up, the player wins $2. Otherwise, the player wins nothing.

    a. If it costs $1 to play the Nickel Game, how much could a player expect to win or lose if he or she plays the game 12 times? Explain your reasoning.

    b. At next year's carnival, the game committee wants to charge prices that will allow players to break even. How much should they charge to play the Nickel Game? Explain your reasoning.

3. In the Ring Toss game, a player tosses a ring at a group of bottles. If the ring goes over a bottle, the player wins a prize. The attendant at the Ring Toss game tells Ben that his chances of winning are 50% because when Ben tosses a ring, it will either go over a bottle or it will not. Do you believe the attendant? Explain your reasoning.

Investigation 1

1. a. $\frac{3}{8}$ b. $\frac{1}{8}$ c. $\frac{4}{8}$

    d. i. $\frac{2}{7}$ ii. $\frac{1}{7}$ iii. $\frac{4}{7}$

    e. The probabilities are theoretical because they are obtained by analyzing the possible outcomes rather than by experimentation.

2. a. $\frac{6}{20}$ b. $\frac{2}{20}$ c. $\frac{8}{20}$

    d. $\frac{4}{20}$ e. The probabilities are experimental because they are based on the results of trials.

    f. 3 yellow, 1 green, 4 red, 2 blue; Since the experimental probability of drawing yellow is $\frac{6}{20}$, or $\frac{3}{10}$, we can predict that 3 of the 10 blocks are yellow. In a similar way, we can predict that 1 out of 10 is green, 4 out of 10 are red, and 2 out of 10 are blue.

3. a. 0, since no combination of 5 coins that includes 3 pennies totals 27 cents.

    b. 0, since the four other coins would have to have a value of 2¢, which is impossible.

4. $\frac{1}{2}$; For each flip, regardless of the previous flips, the probability that the coin will land tails up is $\frac{1}{2}$.

Investigation 2

1. a.   Die 2   b. $\frac{4}{16}$

	+	1	2	3	4
	1	2	3	4	5
Die 1	2	3	4	5	6
	3	4	5	6	7
	4	5	6	7	8

    c. $\frac{3}{16}$ d. $\frac{2}{16}$

    e. The game is fair because the probability of an even outcome ($\frac{1}{8}$) equals the probability of an odd outcome ($\frac{1}{8}$).

    f. This is not unusual, since you would expect that 1 roll in 16, or, equivalently, 2 rolls in 32, would total 8.

2. a. 13 out of 52, or $\frac{1}{4}$

    b. 3; The probability of drawing a club is $\frac{1}{4}$, so you could expect $\frac{1}{4}$ of the 12 cards, or 3 cards, to be clubs.

    c. 4; After removing diamonds from the deck, 13 of the remaining 39 cards, or 1 card in 3, are clubs. So you could expect $\frac{1}{3}$ of the 12 cards, or 4 cards, to be clubs.

    d. The probabilities are theoretical because they are obtained by analyzing the possible outcomes.

© Dale Seymour Publications®

Investigation 3

1. a. $\frac{9}{36}$

   b. $\frac{4}{36}$ c. $\frac{12}{36}$

   d. $\frac{11}{36}$ e. experimental

   f. Students' spinners should have 4 regions—labeled 1, 2, 3, and 4—with relative areas $\frac{1}{4}$, $\frac{1}{12}$, $\frac{1}{3}$, and $\frac{1}{3}$. Specific arrangements of the four regions will vary.

2. a. $\frac{7}{20} = 35\%$ b. $\frac{5}{20} = 25\%$ c. $\frac{5}{20} = 25\%$

   d. $\frac{3}{20} = 15\%$ e. $\frac{15}{20} = 75\%$ f. $\frac{13}{20} = 65\%$

   g. yes; Each girl would have a 50% chance of winning.

Investigation 4

1. a. $\frac{1}{12}$ b. $\frac{1}{6}$ c. $\frac{1}{12}$

   d. Yes, because *KL* and *KM* are equally likely to be selected.

   e. About 4 times; The probability of selecting *AEJI* is $\frac{1}{12}$. So, out of 50 paths, we would expect $\frac{1}{12}$ (50) ≈ 4 to be *AEJI*.

2. a. $\frac{1}{5}$; B is 1 of the 5 letter choices.

   b. $\frac{1}{6}$; Region B is $\frac{1}{6}$ of the area.

   c. The answers are different because the answer to part b was determined by finding the area of region B relative to the area of the whole, and the answer to part a was determined by considering B as one of 5 equally likely outcomes.

   d. $\frac{3}{4}$; There is a $\frac{1}{4}$ chance of hitting region C since it is $\frac{1}{4}$ of the area. So, the probability of *not* hitting region C is $1 - \frac{1}{4} = \frac{3}{4}$.

   e. $\frac{1}{12}$; Region D is half the size of region B.   f. About 33 since E is $\frac{1}{3}$ of the total area.

3. a. $\frac{3}{36}$, or $\frac{1}{12}$ b. $\frac{1}{36}$ c. $\frac{10}{36}$, or $\frac{5}{18}$

   d. $\frac{32}{36}$ or $\frac{8}{9}$, since the probability of rolling a 1 or 6 is $\frac{4}{36}$ or $\frac{1}{9}$.

Answer Keys

Investigation 5

1. a. $\frac{38}{75}$ based on her prior record

    b. 2 or 3; $\frac{38}{75} \times 5 \approx 2.5$

    c. $\frac{6}{10} \times 80 = 48$

2. a. $\frac{2}{5} \times \frac{2}{5} \times \frac{2}{5} = \frac{8}{125}$

    b. 6, since we would expect Aaron to make 3 of every 4 spares.

    c. $\frac{3}{5} \times \frac{1}{4} = \frac{3}{20}$

    d. i. $\frac{2}{5} \times 30 = 12$

    ii. $\frac{3}{5} \times \frac{3}{4} \times 30 = \frac{9}{20} \times 30 = \frac{27}{2} = 13\frac{1}{2}$, so you could expect him to get 13 or 14 spares.

    iii. $\frac{3}{5} \times \frac{1}{4} \times 30 = \frac{3}{20} \times 30 = \frac{9}{2} = 4\frac{1}{2}$, so you could expect him to get 4 or 5 opens.

Investigation 6

1. a. 12, 18, 24, 30, 36, 42, 48, 54, 60, 66, 72

    b. The probability of an odd number is 0. The probability of an even number is 1.

    c. The game is unfair, since the outcome is always even.

2. a. $\frac{5}{26}$ b. $\frac{21}{26}$ c. lose $1.50; It costs $26 \times \$0.25 = \$6.50$ to play. The winnings from 5 games are $5.00.

3. a. $\frac{9}{36} = \frac{1}{4}$

    b. $0; It costs $20 \times \$1 = \$20$ to play. The player can be expected to win $20 \times \frac{1}{4} = 5$ times, or $5 \times \$4 = \$20$.

    c. The game is fair since expected winnings and losings are the same.

Investigation 7

1. a. $\frac{1}{8}$; P(odd) $= \frac{1}{2}$ and $\frac{1}{2} \times \frac{1}{2} \times \frac{1}{2} = \frac{1}{8}$

    b. $\frac{1}{8}$; P(even) is the same as P(odd).

    c. $\frac{3}{8}$; There are eight possible combinations of even and odd numbers, and three of these meet the condition: e-o-o, o-e-o, and o-o-e.

2. a. A player can expect to lose $3. It costs $12 to play 12 games. 2 tails come up 3 times for $3; 2 heads come up 3 times for $6. The total winnings are $9.

    b. Based on part a, it should cost $9 to play 12 games, which is $0.75 per game.

3. no; The chances of the ring going over a bottle are not the same as the chances of it missing (i.e., the outcomes are not equally likely).

counting tree A diagram used to determine the number of possible outcomes in a probability situation. The number of final branches is equal to the number of possible outcomes. The counting tree below shows all the possible outcomes for randomly choosing a yellow or red rose and then a white or pink ribbon. The four possible outcomes are listed in the last column.

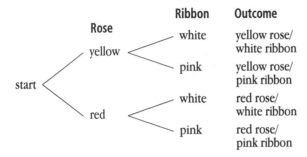

dependent event An event whose probability depends on events that preceded it. For example, suppose two cubes are drawn, one at a time, from a bucket containing two green cubes and one blue cube, and the first cube is not replaced before drawing the second cube. Then, the probability of drawing green on the second draw *depends* on the result of the first draw. If green is drawn first, $P(\text{green}) = \frac{1}{2}$. If blue is drawn first, $P(\text{green}) = 1$.

equally likely events Two or more events that have the same probability of occurring. For example, when you toss a fair coin, heads and tails are equally likely; each has a 50% chance of happening.

event A set of outcomes. For example, when two coins are tossed, getting two matching coins is an event consisting of the outcomes HH and TT.

expected value, long-term average The average payoff over many trials. For example, suppose you are playing a game with two number cubes in which you score 2 points when a sum of 6 is rolled, 1 point for a sum of 3, and 0 points for anything else. If you were to roll the cubes 36 times,

you could expect to roll a sum of 6 about five times and a sum of 3 about twice. This means that you could expect to score $(5 \times 2) + (2 \times 1) = 12$ points for 36 rolls, an average of $\frac{12}{36} = \frac{1}{3}$ point per roll. This is the expected value of a roll.

experimental probability A probability that is determined through experimentation. For example, you could find the experimental probability of getting a head when you toss a coin by tossing a coin many times and keeping track of the outcomes. The experimental probability would be the ratio of the number of heads to the total number of tosses, or trials. Experimental probabilities are used to predict behavior over the long run.

fair game A game in which each player has the same chance of winning. The probability of winning a two-person fair game is $\frac{1}{2}$. An unfair game can be made fair by adjusting the scoring system, or the payoffs. For example, suppose you play a game in which two fair coins are tossed. You score when both coins land heads up; otherwise, your opponent scores. The probability that you will score is $\frac{1}{4}$, and the probability that your opponent will score is $\frac{3}{4}$. To make the game fair, you might adjust the scoring system so that you receive 3 points each time you score and your opponent receives 1 point when he or she scores.

independent event An event whose probability does not depend on events that preceded it. If you draw a cube from a box of variously colored cubes and replace your cube after the draw, then each draw is an independent event.

Law of Large Numbers This law states, in effect, that the more trials of an experiment that are conducted, the more the experimental probability will approximate the theoretical probability.

outcome A possible result of an action. For example, when a number cube is rolled, the possible outcomes are 1, 2, 3, 4, 5, and 6.

payoff The number of points (or dollars or the like) a player in a game receives for a particular event.

probability A number between 0 and 1 that describes the likelihood that an event will occur. For example, a fair number cube is rolled. There is one way out of six possibilities that a 2 can be rolled, so the probability of rolling a 2 is $\frac{1}{6}$. The probability of a certain event is 1, while the probability of an event that cannot occur is 0.

random events Events whose outcomes are uncertain when viewed individually, but which may exhibit a predictable pattern when observed over many trials. For example, when you roll a fair number cube, you have no way of knowing what the next roll will be, but you do know that, over the long run, you will roll each number on the cube about the same number of times.

sample space The set of all possible outcomes in a probability situation. When you flip two coins, the sample space consists of four outcomes: HH, HT TH, and TT.

theoretical probability A probability obtained by analyzing a situation. If all the outcomes are equally likely, you can find a theoretical probability of an event by listing all the possible outcomes and then finding the ratio of the number of outcomes in which you are interested to the total number of outcomes. For example, there are 36 possible equally likely outcomes (number pairs) when two fair number cubes are rolled. Of these, six have a sum of 7, so the probability of rolling a sum of 7 is $\frac{6}{36}$, or $\frac{1}{6}$.

Index

Index

Index